SuperWellness™

Become Your Own Best Healer

Dr. Edith Ubuntu Chan
Foreword by Wim Hof

Disclaimer

This book introduces the reader to a wide range of general wellness and lifestyle practices. It does not claim to diagnose, treat, or cure any medical conditions. This book is not intended to substitute for the services of a trained health care practitioner. Always consult the appropriate doctor or therapist, especially with regards to any symptoms that may require diagnosis and medical attention.

If you choose to apply the ideas and practices contained herein, you are taking full responsibility for your actions, risks, and results. The author, The School of DTW LLC, and its affiliates disclaim all responsibility for any adverse effects that may result directly or indirectly from the information contained in this book.

In other words, please be safe. Use sound judgment and don't do anything silly and hurt yourself. Always consult your doctor(s) or appropriate health professional(s) before engaging in any changes in your health regimen.

First Edition 2017

Paperback ISBN: 978-0-9994360-1-1
Kindle eBook ISBN: 978-0-9994360-2-8

Printed in the United States of America

Cover design by Stephan Wilmas & Dr. Edith Ubuntu Chan

Published by:
The School of Dan Tian Wellness, LLC
638 Stanyan St. San Francisco, CA 94117

For more information about the author Dr. Edith Ubuntu Chan, or for training opportunities, speaking engagements, podcast or media interviews, please visit: www.DrEdithUbuntu.com

This book is dedicated to all the Trailblazers, Gamechangers, and Pioneers that are ushering in a new way for humanity.

Keep shining your light.
Your badassery is much needed.
This book is for YOU.

Deep gratitude for the many "giants" upon whose shoulders I ride - my teachers, mentors, friends, and colleagues around the world. Thank you for your example and inspiration.

Special gratitude for my husband David & our wonder-boy Kabreem for cheering me, nourishing me and loving me always.

CONTENTS

BEFORE YOU START – A WARNING
THIS IS NOT YOUR GRANDPA'S BOOK

Hello Visionary Game-Changers and Pioneers,

Welcome to your SuperWellness. Before you begin, please know that this is not your "normal" book. It's a powerful journey of transformation. It's my intention that you'll be uplifted, empowered and inspired, and we'll have tons of fun together.

But first, a warning: the content of this book will cause you to question many things about our world and look at your life from a bold new perspective. This book is for those who are ready to question the status quo, break free from old limitations, and be in the driver's seat of life again. It's for Visionary Pioneers who have the courage to rise above the standard norms of society.

In other words, this book is <u>not</u> for everybody.

I'll ask you some big questions and share powerful ideas, tools, and strategies. But don't take my word for it. Please test everything out for yourself. Keep only what resonates for you. Throw away what doesn't work. No dogma here. **You're the boss of your life.** You decide what works or doesn't work for you.

We'll take a holistic 360° survey of your lifestyle and self-care. You'll discover how natural and easy it is to create true vibrant health and lifelong well-being. As you experience this journey of self-empowerment, you'll start to see the world from a whole new perspective.

People tell me it's like getting an operating system upgrade. You'll tap into exciting new possibilities and expand your worldview. **Just like taking the "Red Pill" in The Matrix, once you see, there's no going back.**

So are you ready to massively upgrade your health? To take back control of your life? If so, this book is for you.

Welcome to the new world of SuperWellness.

You're going to LOVE it here!

HOW THIS BOOK IS ORGANIZED

Life is precious. Your time is valuable. My goal is to give you enormous value in a fun and joyful way, with minimal time. This book contains a treasure-trove of potent life-changing information that you can put into practice right away.

Here's how our journey is organized:

- **Introduction** - Why SuperWellness? The surprising backstory.
- **Part 1: The Awakening** - Ask critical questions; bust the five greatest myths.
- **Part 2: The Recalibration** - Journey through the Six Dimensions of H.E.A.L.T.H..
- **Part 3: The Arrival** - Put it all together for your journey of SuperWellness mastery.

Each chapter includes interactive questions for your contemplation as well as "SuperWellness Lab" activities. It's my intention that you'll feel confident to implement these power tools right away.

CONGRATULATIONS and WELCOME to the exciting new world of SuperWellness.

Thank you for giving yourself this gift of true vibrant health and lifelong well-being.

Let's start upgrading your life… today.

CELEBRATE! CLAIM YOUR SURPRISE BONUSES!

As you can already see, this book is not like all those other books people have laying around for casual toilet reading. (*Hey, I'm a holistic doctor - none of it is TMI for me!*) Instead, it was designed to be an interactive experience, so that you have the tools to supercharge your energy, upgrade your life, connect with community, and have lots of fun in the process.

As my gift to you, I've created a collection of online resources and video guides to accompany you as action steps for each chapter. This book gives you the understanding and frameworks, while the online downloads and videos support you with guided practice. Please enjoy these gifts from my heart to yours. It's my honor to accompany you on this life-changing journey!

Claim Your Surprise Bonuses at:
www.SuperWellness.com/BookBonuses

Foreword
by Wim Hof

Human beings are designed to be strong, happy, and healthy.

But our modern lifestyle has disconnected us from our inner power. By acclimatizing to all the comforts and conveniences, we have unwittingly lost our natural strength. People are suffering from chronic pain and illness. It's become "normal" to be stressed out, tired, obese, or depressed. Healthcare costs are skyrocketing, but people are getting sicker and sicker.

It's time for change.

With conscious breathing, mind training, and environmental conditioning, we can re-awaken our natural healing power. We can tap into abilities previously thought to be "superhuman." Our capacity to adapt to nature's elements, to thermoregulate, to feel strong, happy, and healthy - this does not require decades of training. We can tap into it in just a few short days.

To me, "Feeling is understanding." When you have the direct experience, you know it.

Of course I'm not the first person to discover these possibilities. Yogis, qigong masters, ancient teachers taught this across millennia. But I am the first western person to bring it to scientific inquiry. Take away all the speculation.

Through scientific studies, we have proven that human beings can influence his/her nervous system, immune system, and endocrine system - far deeper than ever thought possible. We've proven that the so-called "autonomic nervous system" is no longer "autonomous." First-time mountaineers can summit Kilimanjaro in previously inconceivable record time. Countless cases of so-called "incurable" conditions have been improved through simple breathing and training practices. Study after study, we're blowing our minds.

We are re-writing the medical textbooks.

1

But being a pioneer and questioning society's norms is not always easy. Luckily I'm not alone.

Dr. Edith Ubuntu Chan is my sister of light. Like me, her work unites ancient wisdom with modern science. As a Holistic Chinese Medicine doctor, with a Math and Engineering background from Harvard, she has the unique ability to integrate East and West. With her years in meditation, yoga, qigong and endurance sports, she has a deep understanding grounded in direct personal experience. She's a real treasure. One-of-a-kind.

Even more, Dr. Edith carries an infectious joy and love for life! She brings a pure heart and conscious intention into everything she does. When you meet her, you'll see. Her love and light is contagious.

When I travel around the world speaking, people often ask about lifestyle topics outside the Wim Hof Method. Topics like: nutrition, hydration, fasting, sleep, earthing, sunlight, and mindfulness. Now I can just recommend that they read SuperWellness. It's all in here!

Dr. Edith will give you a holistic 360° survey of your lifestyle. She lays out the science, then guides you into having your own direct personal experience. There is no dogma here. She shows you the scientific research, then brings you back to your inner wisdom. You'll decide for yourself. "Feeling is understanding."

Maybe you're sick and tired and ready to get healthy. Maybe you're a "biohacker" looking for your next level. Or maybe you're a professional doctor, here to upgrade your toolkit. There's something in this book for everyone. You will be inspired and empowered.

SuperWellness is a great gift to our world. Dr. Edith Ubuntu Chan is a true pioneer and my dear friend. I'm so happy to share this mission with her. The mission to empower every human being to be extraordinary.

Love,

Wim Hof

September 21st 2017

Wim Hof is internationally renowned for his 26x Guinness World Records, including countless ice endeavors that range from being up to his neck in a tank filled with ice for 1hour53minutes, to swimming long distances under polar ice, to running a marathon barefoot, and climbing Everest in nothing more than shorts and shoes. He became known by the nickname "The Iceman." Wim is showing the world that our human body is capable of far more than we previously thought, once you tap into the flow within your inner state of being. Currently, his time and energy are devoted to scientific research and passing the Wim Hof Method on to others, so that everyone can experience far more that they previously thought possible. Wim believes that through the right training, you can strengthen your inner nature and prevent disease. He believes that everybody deserves to feel strong, happy, and healthy. Learn more at: www.wimhofmethod.com.

INTRODUCTION

"Nothing is too wonderful to be true, if it be consistent with the laws of nature."

~ Michael Faraday ~

WHY DO WE NEED SUPERWELLNESS?

Questions for you:

Have you ever struggled with a health issue and spent countless hours researching on the internet, reading article after article, vetting all the so-called "experts" out there, only to find endless streams of conflicting information?

Maybe you've gone from practitioner to practitioner, trying everything from conventional to alternative treatments, taking expensive supplements, investing time, energy, and money. But you're wondering - what's really helping and what's not helping?

Have you ever been told that to be healthy, you need to follow a regimented diet and exercise program - one that requires vigilant tracking, willpower, deprivation, and sacrifice?

Or maybe you've been frustrated by an experience with a health practitioner. You were unhappy with their care, but didn't feel you had any other choices. You felt stuck, and you wish there were more options.

Sound familiar? Most of us have been in one or more of these scenarios. You may even be thinking: *"Oh my goodness - (E) ALL of the above!"*

We all care deeply about our health. It's our #1 priority. But does it have to be so darn expensive? So complicated? So frustrating and time consuming?

Here in the U.S., we all know that healthcare costs are skyrocketing out-of-control. In 2016, the U.S. spent $3.4 trillion on healthcare. That's a whopping $10,000+ per person![1] Yet we have shorter lifespans and higher rates of illness and disease than any other industrialized nation.[2] In other words, we spend more money on healthcare than any other country, but we're the sickest of all the industrialized nations.

To call it a broken system is an understatement.

Exasperated by these trends, many of us are seeking alternatives. We're reading online, paying out-of-pocket for nutritional supplements, and exploring alternative therapies in search of better outcomes. We all know that drugs and surgery are not the only solutions out there. But to be healthy, we're told we must follow those rigid and militant diet and exercise plans that take all the fun out of life. Don't you think there should be a better way?

Imagine:

- A new world, where getting healthy is Fun, Joyful and requires Zero deprivation.

- A world where the best healing tools are also Free, Simple, and Abundantly available.

- A life where you can become stress-free, get the best sleep, lose those pesky pounds without dieting, heal faster, look radiant, have amazing energy, and enjoy more quality time with your friends, family, and kids.

- You can become your own best Healer. How much time, energy, or money would you save? What beautiful things could you do with all that extra time and money?

Think this sounds too good to be true? **It's time to think again.**

We're about to embark on a wild and beautiful journey together, a journey of self-empowerment and self-discovery. In these pages, you'll discover the **truth** about your health, which is far more exciting and empowering than we've ever been told.

Over my last 15 years as a Holistic Medicine doctor, supporting the healing program of thousands of patients, we uncovered something so exciting, so mind-blowing and so paradigm-busting, I wanted to shout it off rooftops everywhere I went.

"The truth about our health is far more empowering than we've ever been told!"

Throughout the course of 35,000+ hours of clinical practice, treating a broad spectrum of patients from simple aches and pains, to complex or serious chronic health conditions, we routinely saw that **the greatest healing results come from shockingly simple self-care strategies.** Whether it's an elite athlete striving for a new record, or a patient struggling with serious chronic illness, or a "health-nut / biohacker" seeking the next level of human performance, the same fundamental self-care tools and strategies gave us the most incredible results.

As a health practitioner, this caused me to question everything.

Could it be, that the most potent and powerful healing tools are also the cheapest and most easily accessible ones?

Has our world made health and healing far too elusive? Far too expensive? Far too complicated?

What if... "health and wellness" is actually much simpler than we've been told?

Prior to Holistic Medicine, I studied Applied Mathematics and Engineering at Harvard University and spent a few years working in Software. The engineering nerd in me LOVES finding patterns and algorithms. With my background as a competitive athlete from age 15 to 35, I spent decades training, experimenting and obsessing about optimal human performance. So with the same geeky excitement that people get up on Sunday mornings to complete their crossword puzzles, I devoted all my free time to research and systematize these findings. I distilled the best gems from all the years of clinical experience into simple principles that delivered massive results for our patients.

Our holistic medicine clinic became known in the community for these phenomenal results. Many colleagues and graduate students came to study with me expecting to learn some complicated or expensive treatment protocols. But time and time again, they were amazed to discover that **our** "secret sauce" was so shockingly simple! We developed an elegant approach to helping patients rebuild their healthy foundation, using carefully curated self-care tools that are fun, simple, and powerful. The results wowed everyone.

The biggest shocker was this: re-establishing a balanced lifestyle through these self-care tools accounted for not just a small boost, but often **the vast majority of the overall healing**. As patients continued to leverage their one-on-one work with professional practitioners, they often reported faster and longer-lasting results.

"We realized we were onto something HUGE."

Beyond the phenomenal results, we enjoyed a far more fulfilling and rewarding relationship with our patients and community. Patients were thrilled to be self-empowered and save enormous amounts of time and money. And we're deeply honored to witness such life-changing transformations. A win-win-win for everybody.

Some might imagine that getting faster results was bad for business. But of course that's not true. The exact opposite happened.

Word traveled, and our clinic was blessed with rapid growth and long waitlists. We knew we were onto something big and wanted to serve many more people. The individual one-on-one clinical practice was always fully booked; it limited how many people we could serve. So in 2012, we launched the very first live in-person SuperWellness class, sharing this revolutionary new approach with our local community in San Francisco.

In SuperWellness, we take an expansive and holistic 360° survey of your lifestyle, going far beyond the old "Diet and Exercise" paradigm, to re-establish a true and lasting foundation for health. We empower each participant to become their own best Healer, with the most potent tools and strategies, and to be in the driver's seat of their life again. **As a natural side-effect, participants tell us they experience less stress, more energy, better sleep, more joy, peace, and clarity.** They look and feel radiant, and often heal faster from various ailments. Most importantly, they discover a more fearless and confident approach to life.

"SuperWellness is a holistic 360° lifestyle upgrade - going far beyond the old 'Diet and Exercise' paradigm. It's a revolutionary new formula for health."

Participants of the SuperWellness program included patients and health practitioners alike (e.g. health & wellness professionals, MDs, nurses, PhD scientists, medical researchers, caretakers, and many "doctor-moms" and "doctor-dads"). They raved about their transformational journey to their friends and community, and word spread naturally through word-of-mouth.

With each and every iteration, we had the opportunity to learn and refine the program. We discovered that the friendships and social-learning environment enhanced the healing experience in dramatic ways. **Community is powerful medicine!**

About eight-to-ten iterations in, we hit a big jackpot.

We found the precise formula - an exact step-by-step sequence that yielded the most potent synergistic results. This gave birth to the now famous **Six-Dimensions of "H.E.A.L.T.H.."** Each component of H.E.A.L.T.H. supported the others in elegant and synergistic ways. (Full details of "H.E.A.L.T.H." are in Part II of the book). We were blown away by the results.

Here's what some SuperWellness participants have said:

- *"My Energy is unbelievable. I feel truly <u>Alive</u> for the first time in 20 years!"*
- *"This program has done for me in a matter of weeks what other healing modalities could not in years. So grateful."*
- *"My aches and pains are gone. But most of all, this has added so much Joy and Optimism to my life, I would definitely recommend to anyone!"*
- *"What a wonderfully freeing feeling… [to] break free from food cravings. 10 pounds in 6 weeks in a painless transformation."*
- *"Learning how to deal with my stress, how to take better care of myself. Not just my physical body, but also my mind, my emotions and spirit. It was fantastic."*

- *"It gave me the fundamental understanding that the source of health and well-being is within each of us, which is the most powerful gift that anyone can give you."*
- *"So many great takeaways. It upgraded my entire approach to health. I feel empowered and inspired to take control of my well-being for the rest of my life. An incredible gift!"*
- *"A joyful and soulful experience. I hope many more are privileged to participate in this journey."*

It's worth reiterating that **SuperWellness does not diagnose or treat any medical conditions.** It's never a substitute for professional consultations with a doctor. *Please always consult a professional healthcare provider as appropriate, especially for any symptoms that require diagnosis and professional attention.*

Instead, SuperWellness gives you a powerful lifestyle formula that cultivates true vibrant health and lifelong well-being. We are not addressing any specific medical conditions, yet we notice that faster healing often takes place as a pleasant "side-effect."

When people receive their therapeutic treatments with professional healthcare practitioners, they often report seeing better, faster, and longer-lasting results. This is because SuperWellness creates a solid and lasting foundation for your health, which naturally supports everything else.

So SuperWellness is many things: It's a holistic lifestyle program. It's a journey of self-empowerment. It's a formula for cultivating Health. And it's a revolution; a much-needed revolution given the state of our world today, don't you agree?

"SuperWellness is the true healthcare reform we've all been waiting for."

Today, we're at a powerful turning-point moment in human history. With regards to our health, it is no longer possible to sit idly, waiting for a broken system to fix itself. The solution lies within each of us, supporting and empowering one another to take control of our own well-being.

SuperWellness gives you the precise formula to do that. The best gems and tools are now in your hands.

Before we move on, I'd like to take a moment to honor you for being the visionary and outside-the-box thinker that you are. Being a pioneer is not always easy. I want to recognize the uniquely beautiful journey that you've been through that made you the person you are today. This book is not for the average joe. The fact that you are still reading means you're amongst a small and powerful group of pioneers and leaders ushering in a new way of living for your family, your community, and our world. You're a game-changer, and you're in good company here.

Of course, we both know that you didn't become the person that you are today, just overnight. It takes experience, wisdom, insights, and tremendous courage to rise above the standard norms of society.

So in preparation for the next section, please give yourself a huge congratulations for the challenges that you have already overcome. Our world needs your wisdom and strength more than ever before.

JOURNAL ACTIVITY - CONTEMPLATIONS

- Q: Looking back on your journey, what was the greatest turning point moment that led you to be the out-of-box thinker that you are today?

- Q: What do you feel is the #1 struggle that you've overcome? How did you find the strength and wisdom to rise above it?

- Q: How can you tap into that strength and wisdom more consistently, to meet the challenges ahead?

- Q: What is a major challenge that you're currently facing? If SuperWellness gives you greater energy, less stress, more peace and clarity, how will it assist you in rising above this current challenge faster and more elegantly?

Please take a moment to jot down your answers.

In the next section, I'd love to share with you the backstory of SuperWellness. It's a story about embracing life's struggles and the surprising magic that unfolds when we follow our hearts, follow our dreams. If it were not for the strange and surprising events that led to the birth of SuperWellness, this book would not be here today.

Often it is life's greatest challenges that bring us the greatest gifts. Join me on this journey.

THE BACKSTORY OF SUPERWELLNESS: EMBRACING LIFE'S MAGIC & MYSTERY

There are no accidents in life. If you're reading this page, it's likely because you're going through a major transition or pursuing big dreams. This section is especially dedicated to you.

Change is not always easy. Sometimes we fall flat on our face. If you're feeling challenged by life's curveballs, please know that you're not alone. Our community is here for you and with you. I invite you to honor the journey and embrace the struggle. Take lovingly good care of yourself (with SuperWellness tools and beyond), and trust in life's innate intelligence.

Often it is only in hindsight that we can see the greater tapestry at work.

Life has taught me that **the quickest path from point A to point B is not a straight line.** Instead, it's the one that pushes us to grow and learn the quickest. It's the one that awakens us to life's most powerful lessons. It's the one that breaks us free of old limitations, so that we can shine fully and serve others with the wisdom and insights gained through this trial by fire.

As I look back on the journey that led to this book, I'm overwhelmed in waves of gratitude at the magic and mystery of it all. Life conspired and groomed me through a series of strange events, so that I would feel the intensity of pain and suffering that we all share, question the status quo, search deeply for answers, and ultimately step into my passion of helping others live extraordinary lives.

THE SURPRISING #1 FAQ AT OUR CLINIC

At my Holistic Medicine practice in San Francisco, it always used to surprise me that the #1 question patients ask is not: *"Dr. Edith, can you help me with this X condition?"* or *"What foods should I eat or not eat?"* or *"How many treatment sessions will we need?"*

Instead, the #1 most frequently asked question is:

"Dr. E, how did you go from studying Math at Harvard to becoming a Holistic Chinese Medicine healer?"

One of the greatest discoveries over my last 15 years of clinical experience is this - whenever patients are struggling with a health condition, it also motivates them to ask bigger questions about life. Pain, illness, or injury are powerful opportunities for learning and growth. They open us to exciting new possibilities in all aspects of life, if we choose to take advantage of that opportunity.

Most of us are deeply restless for change right now. Nearly everyone who comes to my clinic expresses a major dissatisfaction with the status quo of our world. Many of us are feeling stuck in our careers, stuck in our health, stuck in our relationships, stuck in the state of chronic stress, anxiety, and overwhelm. In every area of life, we are seeing the unsustainable ways of our society. Deep in our hearts, deep in our souls, we know there's a much better way. We know it's possible to create a life that's more beautiful, more harmonious, more joyful and fulfilling.

Since you're reading this book, I know you're already awake to the problems of our world. You have a deep desire to create a better life for yourself, for your family and community. Please take a moment to honor yourself. Pat yourself on the back! It takes guts to chart a new course, to step into your power and shine your light fully.

I hope that my story and the stories of all the SuperWellness heroes in this book will empower you to live a truly Happy, Healthy and Extraordinary life. You deserve it!

Now back to the #1 most frequently asked question:

"Dr. E, how did you go from studying Math at Harvard to becoming a Holistic Chinese Medicine healer?"

My answer: *"It's a good story..."*

When I was a child, my family lived in multicultural Hong Kong - a big bustling city where capitalism and modern technologies were king. My father was a businessman who ran a shipping logistics company and travelled often to the U.S.. My mother was a journalist who left her career to become a stay-at-home mom, to raise my sister and me. We prided ourselves in our modern, urban and scientifically-minded ways of living. We often teased the older generation of Chinese grandmas and grandpas for their old-fashioned and superstitious ways.

One day when I was four years old, my sister (she was six or seven) sprained her ankle. It stayed swollen and painful for weeks and did not heal with any of the conventional treatments. My father also suffered from a back sprain that didn't respond to conventional western treatments. We were blessed to have an uncle who was an MD and an aunt who was a head nurse at the local hospital. So we always received excellent medical care. This saved us many times (like that time when I was a kid and choked on a fish bone, oy!). But in this case with my sister's ankle and my father's back pain, the conventional treatments did not help.

A family friend recommended a Chinese Qigong healer who was known for healing all sorts of aches and pains where conventional medicine had failed. At that time, around 1980, Chinese Medicine was not the popular complementary medicine profession that it is today, even in Hong Kong. The thousands of scientific research studies that we have now were not yet published (e.g. studies on energy healing, Qigong, acupuncture, herbal medicine, nutrition, meditation, breathwork, etc. did not exist yet). There were no board exams or strict licensure requirements as there are now. There was no internet, no Yelp reviews, no PubMed research database.

It was 1980. Think Beta-max and VHS tapes. And those velour warm-up tracksuits. You know the ones - with the matching tops and bottoms. My mom loved dressing me in those velour warm-ups.

Back in those days, to become a Chinese healer, one would enter into a traditional apprenticeship with an old master, usually for decades. (*"Wax-on, wax-off, paint-the fence, etc."*) Some old masters seemed to have real demonstrable healing skills, while others were probably scams and quacks. My parents had exhausted all their healing options in conventional medicine and were desperate for help. So with a BIG dose of skepticism, my family went to visit this Qigong healer.

I tagged along for the exciting adventure and wore my favorite purple velour warm-ups for the occasion.

What happened next would set the trajectory of my life decades later.

The Qigong master was a jolly monk with an orange robe and a friendly smile. I remember poking his big round belly. Poke poke. Giggles. He called his belly the "Dan Tian", where he cultivated "Qi" for healing people. "Dan" means medicine or elixir, and "Tian" means field. So "Dan Tian" is the place where you cultivate a field of medicine for healing.

It all sounded like a foreign language to me. But I was mesmerized. Fascinated. This was by far the coolest thing I ever experienced in my four years on earth.

In one single session, the Qigong master "emitted healing Qi" from his hands. My sister's ankle swelling came down, and the pain was gone. Yes. One session. My father's back pain was also healed in one session. None of us could believe our eyes. As a 4-year-old child, this seemed like magic to me.

I had seen this "Qi" depicted through special effects in martial arts movies (you know the kind - the "Crouching Tiger, Hidden Dragon" genre). But this was the first time I saw it in real life, with my own eyes.

From that day, I declared to all the adults in our family:

"When I grow up, I want to be a traditional Chinese healer."

The adults - my parents, aunts and uncles - all chuckled. They had the best intentions for me and responded unanimously: *"That's not possible. You can't make any decent living doing that. You don't wanna go apprentice with some old healer. You gotta go to school, get good grades, so you can get a good job when you grow up."*

"Go to school. Get good grades. Get a good job." Heard that one before?

But I was a stubborn kid. For months I didn't back down. It was just too amazing what I saw. I was determined to become a Chinese healer when I grew up. I had romantic ideas about practicing in the old tradition, just like in the movies. But after endless negotiations with all the adults, I was getting nowhere. This healer thing was simply unacceptable to them. Then one day I acquiesced and said: *"Ok fine. If I can't be a Chinese healer, then I'm going to be an Astronaut instead."*

As you might imagine, my parents were thrilled that I finally quit the Chinese healer "phase." Being an astronaut is far more practical than being some Chinese Qi healer, right? So they encouraged me. To be an astronaut, I must to be exceptional at math, science, and engineering. So I set about becoming the best kid in my class at math and science. I played with home science experiments and tinkered with engineering projects whenever I wasn't in school. My parents were amazingly supportive with the endless explosions and messes I made in the kitchen. In school, I became exceptional in math, skipping two or three years ahead of my grade level. This eventually opened many doors and helped me to be accepted at the top boarding school in the U.S. called Phillips Exeter Academy, and later to Harvard University.

My gifts in math and science opened so many exciting doors that eventually I forgot about trying to become an astronaut or a Chinese healer. (Also once puberty hit, I was distracted by all the cute boys in school!) Nonetheless, that one amazing day as a four-year-old child, watching the Qigong Master heal with "Qi" altered my perception of human possibilities - forever.

Seeing the results of that Qigong healing planted the seed that maybe, just maybe, our modern science and conventional western medicine does not have all the answers. Even more importantly, it gave me the feeling that **perhaps we human beings have no idea just how powerful and extraordinary we really are.**

If that Qigong healing is possible, **what else is possible that we never learn in the textbooks?**

Now fast forward 20 years later - to the first dot-com boom.

Step into the era of "The Matrix", "Harry Potter", "Lord of the Rings", "Crouching Tiger, Hidden Dragon", and "Galaxy Quest."

I was in my mid-20s, living the American dream. Great Silicon Valley job, nice salary, stock options, and a fancy loft apartment in San Francisco with the high ceilings, chrome appliances, and granite counter-tops.

The world was my oyster. I graduated *Magna Cum Laude* in Applied Mathematics from Harvard University. My hardworking immigrant parents couldn't be more proud. At work, I was rising through the ranks and awarded "Employee of the Year", enjoying recognition from all directions from CXOs to managers to friends and family.

Everything was picture perfect.

There's just one problem, one very big problem.

I was chronically stressed out and unhappy, and it was making me sick.

Like other twenty-somethings striving to make it big in tech, I lived by the motto *"Work Hard, Play Hard."* This means 60-to-80 hour work-weeks meeting high-pressure deadlines. Lots of coffee and Red Bulls during the day, then partying and boozing on evenings and weekends to blow off steam. On some level, I knew this lifestyle was not sustainable. But all my friends were doing it. With stock options and IPOs left and right, many friends were already paper millionaires. It's what we all did: climbing the tech corporate ladder and dreaming of hitting the stock-options and IPO jackpot for an early retirement.

Every shot of espresso was one shot closer to that dot-com millionaire dream.

But with the great salary also came ten-to-fifteen unwanted pounds, digestive issues, headaches, poor sleep, debilitatingly painful menstrual cramps, allergies, acne breakouts, and frequent colds/flus from the high stress. My first white hair sprouted up at age 24. Was I aging prematurely?

When I told friends or doctors about the various health ailments, nobody seemed very concerned since it was not life-threatening. It's just stress, they'd say.

So I shrugged it off as normal.

"Oh well. I'm an adult now. Stress is part of life. Just take some ibuprofen."

Then one day, I was invited to sit-in on a senior meeting at my company. I've always had the gift of translating complex technical concepts into layperson-friendly terms that everyone can understand. In fact, my job here was to do exactly that - turning business requirements into technical requirements and vice-versa. Because of this inter-disciplinary skill, I would sometimes be invited to meetings far beyond my ranks.

This was my first time taking part in such a high level meeting. I was overjoyed at the opportunity to rub shoulders with senior leaders. Some of them were industry legends with jaw-droppingly impressive resumes that I dreamed of achieving one day. Stepping into the meeting, I was giddy with excitement, thinking: *"Wow! These are the people I want to be when I grow up!"*

Little did I know, it would be a major turning point of my life.

Being in this meeting with senior "bigwigs" was a big deal. So I savored the moment, took a deep breath and scanned the room. The smell of the dry-erase white-board, the humming sounds of the projector, the big shiny oval table, and the seating arrangements. I took it all in. I couldn't wait to learn from such experienced "wise elders" so-to-speak.

As soon as I sat down, the romantic soundtrack in my head came to a sudden screeching halt. To my shock and surprise, these accomplished senior "bigwigs" looked far more overworked and stressed out than I ever imagined. As the meeting proceeded, I began to see the intense pressures that they faced - from navigating legal regulations to managing financial expectations. It's all about the bottom-line. This was business after all.

Images started flooding into my mind of a future, older me. Years flashed by; I saw myself climbing the corporate ladder of "success", making a bigger salary but feeling increasingly burnt out, stressed out, and unhappy. I saw myself aging fast and getting sicker and sicker.

With these visions came the shocking realization: I was not making a "living." I was making a "dying."

An inner voice asked: *"Is this really what you want to be when you grow up?"*

In that moment, all the old memories of the Chinese Qigong healer came rushing back in. It had been 20 years, but I could see his orange robe, his round Qi-belly (*"this is my Dan Tian!"*), and his friendly smile as if it had been just yesterday. Rapid-fire images of past, present, future possibilities flashed by at lightning speed. To be honest I stopped paying much attention to the rest of that meeting. As soon as the meeting was adjourned, I returned to my desk and began researching about Chinese Medicine.

To my pleasant surprise, much had changed since I was that little girl in Hong Kong dreaming of apprenticing with a traditional Chinese healer. There were now intensive graduate degree programs in Chinese Medicine all around the world, with medical board exams that regulated the practice of Acupuncture and Traditional Chinese Medicine. Research on modalities like Qigong and Acupuncture was breaking new ground every day. Being a Chinese Medicine healer is now a viable profession, and it turned out the best school in the U.S. was right here in San Francisco.

Just reading the school program catalog made my heart soar! The diversity of coursework was endlessly fascinating to me: Qigong, TaiChi, Nutrition, Herbal Medicine, Acupuncture, Bodywork and Manual therapy, Eastern and Western Internal Medicine, Pharmacology, Herb-Drug Interactions, History of Medicine, Ancient and Modern Healing Philosophies, Patient Counselling techniques, and integrative approaches to Sports Medicine, Orthopedics, Women's Health, Fertility, Immunology, and more. I could hardly contain myself in excitement. I wanted to learn it all!

The inner voice asked: *"Is THIS what you want to be when you grow up?"*

My heart burst in Joy: *"YES! That's me!"*

But change can be so scary. My head immediately started spinning with endless doubts and fears.

So I discussed the idea of changing my career with friends and family. Everyone thought I was crazy. *"That sounds nuts! Why would you walk away from a totally lucrative career in tech to become some sort of hippy healer?"*

At that time, surveys showed that more than half of Chinese Medicine graduates could not make a living doing it professionally. After years of intense study, practice, exams, and more exams, most graduates were not able to sustain their career in Chinese Medicine and would end up going back to their previous work.

The odds were stacked against me. My family was worried. They wanted the best for me and tried to dissuade me in every possible way.

One relative said: *"Why would anyone throw away a perfectly good Harvard brain to become some sort of a quack?"*

My aunt who was head nurse at the hospital tried to convince me so sweetly and caringly: *"Honey, we're all worried. You can't make any decent living doing this Chinese Medicine stuff. Why don't you just become a regular MD? You're so smart, you can get into a good medical school. You'll make much better money as an MD."*

But I was not drawn by money, approval, or fame. The calling came from a far deeper place. **It was an insatiable desire to learn the Truth about life. The Truth about our human potential.** I needed to know: *"How is it that the Qigong master could help patients when conventional western medicine had failed? What else is possible that our world has told us is impossible?"*

Meanwhile, the mounting stress of 60-to-80 hour work-weeks, plus now the dueling voices between my head and my heart was taking its toll. The headaches, the digestive troubles, the menstrual pain, the skin issues, the weight gain. I realized: *"Worse-case scenario, this career change could teach me how to take better care of my health and my family's health. AND it would answer my lifelong curiosity about Qi and the nature of healing. I'm a smart and adaptive person. I could get part-time jobs and make ends meet somehow."*

Moments later, the doubts and fears would return again: *"It's not practical. Maybe they're right. I shouldn't be so irresponsible and stupid. How can I walk away from everything I know?"*

The voices argued back and forth like this for months.

In the end, it was the tragic events of September 11th, 2001 that gave me the big *jolt* I needed to finally take the leap. September 11th shook me to the core, as I'm sure it did all of us. It woke me up to the preciousness of life. Around that time, I began dating a fabulous new guy named David, who was also going through a big career change. He had just left his corporate job to pursue his dream. We could leap into the big scary unknown together.

So with David's encouragement, I gave my notice at work. I moved out of that big expensive loft apartment with the chrome appliances and granite countertops, sold most of my possessions, and downsized massively. Just me, my cat, one suitcase and one bicycle.

San Francisco apartments were never easy to come by, especially now with no job and no income. At that time, David lived simply and frugally in a small 8ft x 8ft room, sharing a house with four college buddies. David was the first "minimalist" I ever met, way before minimalism was even a "thing." He taught me how little we really needed to be happy. So once I decided to leave my tech job. I shed most of my possessions and moved into David's tiny 8ft x 8ft room.

Imagine us - two humans, one cat, my bike, David's bike, a futon bed, a tiny desk, all finagled into his little 8ft x 8ft bedroom. (Lucky for the cat, the room had a door that opened to the back patio of the building.) It was the most ridiculous thing... and we LOVED it!

We have story after story of those crazy days: eating rice-n-beans when finances allowed, but mostly just rice, no beans. A little sauce or seasoning if we got fancy. It was the most happy, joyful, and romantic time of our lives. (Yes, that awesome guy David is now my husband and the father of my boy.)

Shortly after enrolling in school, I was blessed to meet a world-class Qigong master named Dr. Fu, who recently moved to San Francisco from Beijing. Dr. Fu had been groomed in a traditional apprenticeship to become a world-renowned Qigong master and was also a trained shaolin monk. Besides being a master in Qigong healing and traditional manual therapy techniques, he was licensed to practice Acupuncture and herbal medicine. Dr. Fu accepted me as one of his three long-term apprentices in the special way of the old tradition.

For me, being accepted as an apprentice with Dr. Fu was 1000x more precious than getting into Harvard University. My unusual dream since age four was coming true! I won the ultimate cosmic lottery!

I loved everything about this new life - going to school with smart, like-minded people who were out-of-the-box thinkers, then apprenticing with a Qigong master in the way of the old tradition whenever I was not in school.

"Wax-on. Wax-off. Paint the fence." It was everything that I dreamed. I had little money and no possessions. But finally I found a life filled with clarity, love, and fulfillment. It was a deep inner contentment that I had never experienced before.

As a side effect, my "dot-com" health ailments - the headaches, the sleep problems, the digestive troubles, the menstrual cramps, the acne, and more - all gradually faded away.

It took a few more years, but eventually my family who tried so hard to dissuade me from this career change, all came around. They couldn't help but see how happy I was in this new life. Month after month. Year after year. The infectious joy and deep contentment won them over.

I started to help my family heal various aches and pains, especially with the unusually potent methods that Dr. Fu taught me in my apprenticeship outside of school. Because of my studies with Dr. Fu, I was blessed to accumulate 3x the clinical hours and 5x the patient caseloads than is normal within the first four years of a practitioner's training.

Dr. Fu taught me powerful healing techniques that were passed down in the special way of the apprenticeship tradition and not in any textbooks. The results stunned my family - like the time my Uncle from Canada had Frozen Shoulder. He had been doing PT for a year with little results. I was thrilled to help him regain his range-of-motion with only two sessions of manual therapy, qigong, and acupuncture during a brief holiday visit.

My inner joy and the practical healing results spoke for themselves. It became easy for everyone to see the true value of this new life path - far beyond money, recognition, or fame.

So if you're in the midst of a major life transition, and your friends and family are doubting you, I hope that this story opens a fresh new perspective. I've come to see that our friends and family's apparent doubts or "naysaying" is only because they love us and want the best for us. They want us to be healthy and safe. But **nobody knows what passions stir within your heart, or what unusual gifts and potentials lie within you. Only you do.** Friends and family will come around when they see that you're happy, healthy and fulfilled. In the end, your example will also give others the courage to listen to their hearts, explore their passions, and follow their dreams.

Introduction

When you love your life, it's irresistible. It's contagious. Love always wins.

Many patients tell me that hearing the story of my personal struggles is as impactful as the treatments and nutritional advice they receive. Perhaps that's why it's the most frequently asked question in our clinical practice. In times of change, sometimes it's this kind of "nutrition for the soul" that we most need. It's a reminder that life is kind. Life is intelligent. Just on the other side of our struggles is a grand tapestry at work, with unimaginable beauty.

With hindsight today, it's easy to see the perfection of this strange and circuitous journey.

If it weren't for that Qigong experience as a small child, I may not have ignited this lifelong passion to explore the frontiers of our human possibilities. If my parents had allowed me to go off into a traditional apprenticeship as a child, I would not have cultivated my abilities in math and science. I would not have the engineering and analytical background that is so fundamental to my work today. If it weren't for this cross-cultural, multi-faceted, multi-disciplinary journey, I could not be here now, sharing with you the best of East and West.

The stressful years working in tech gave me the most priceless gift of all - learning how to let go of the dueling voices in the head, and listen to the heart. For that, I am forever grateful.

We've shared that SuperWellness was born out of my last 15 years and 35,000+ hours of clinical experience as a Holistic Medicine doctor. But perhaps it's more accurate to say it's the result of my entire life's journey. With the completion of this book, I'm honored to share with you the best lessons learned from all my years as a human being.

Each of us has a uniquely perfect journey. It's my hope that this story, and the stories of other SuperWellness heroes, will inspire you to uncover more of the magic and beauty in your life.

JOURNAL ACTIVITY - CONTEMPLATIONS

Now let's turn the focus on to **your** life story! In preparation for the next chapter, I invite you to contemplate these questions.

- Q: What is the biggest challenge that you're currently facing? Please keep this in mind as you journey through the book, and allow new ideas, inspiration, and solutions for your challenge to arise.

- Q: Five to ten years from now, how might you look back on today's challenge as a surprisingly beautiful gift? What opportunities and gifts could come to you as a result of this challenge?

When you turn the page, we step into Part 1 of our SuperWellness journey: "The Awakening." We will take an objective look at some old limiting beliefs about "health" that society has trained us to buy into. I bought into them too!

You'll find out why these commonly-held beliefs have been derailing us from true vibrant health, rather than empowering us.

Albert Einstein said famously: *"No problem can be solved from the same level of consciousness that created it."* That's why busting these big myths is fundamental on our journey into SuperWellness.

It's going to be a wild and beautiful journey. Ready? Let's dive in.

PART I: THE AWAKENING

"That which is false troubles the heart.
But truth brings joyous tranquility."

~ Rumi ~

H ave you ever heard of the term - "invisible ships" or "ships not seen?" It originated from the lore and ship logs of early European explorers like Christopher Columbus (1492), Ferdinand Magellan (1520), and James Cook (1770). When European explorers first arrived in new lands, they noticed the indigenous peoples did not "see" their large ships that were clearly visible to the human eye in broad daylight. The story goes that, because the concept of these ships was so foreign, they were unrecognizable by the native people's minds. So the ships remained "invisible" until their minds were able to conceptualize it.

Full disclosure: I was not there in 1492, 1520, or 1770. So who knows if this really happened? But the idea of "invisible ships" is fascinating, don't you agree?

Modern day scientists and social psychologists like to borrow this term to refer to **discoveries that are hidden in plain sight**. Our minds sometimes have trouble seeing what is totally obvious. It can remain invisible to us until someone calls it out. Once we can conceptualize it, name it, and see it, it becomes so clear and obvious that we can't believe we didn't see it all along.

Have you ever had that experience? Not seeing something that's right under your nose? It's like when you look frantically all over the house for your keys, only to find that they were in your pocket the whole time. You just have to laugh.

In Part 1 of our SuperWellness journey, "The Awakening," we're going to discover some very simple, profound, and empowering truths about our health.

Most of these will feel like a "ships not seen" situation. You'll laugh and wonder how we could have overlooked them for so long.

A few ideas may seem more bold or even controversial. Questioning old beliefs, even if we know they were false and disempowering, can feel uncomfortable at first. So I invite you to keep an open mind, take your time, and allow the ideas to settle, process, and integrate. As we bust these old myths, you'll feel excited and inspired by brand new possibilities!

In Chapter 1, we'll explore the #1 biggest blind-spot in the world of health and wellness. I'm going to explain **why "Eat Right and Exercise" is not the key** to our health.

"What? No way, Dr. Edith! How can that be? That goes against EVERYTHING I've ever heard!?!"

Yes I know. This one blew my mind too! But it's so fundamental to our understanding of healthy lifestyle that we must address it first. When you read Chapter 1, I think you'll agree it's not as controversial as it sounds, but rather a "ships not seen" situation. We'll also introduce a new approach to healthy living that transcends the old paradigm of "willpower and discipline."

Think it sounds too good to be true? Don't just take my word for it. Read the chapter and decide for yourself.

In Chapter 2, we're going to address **the "Five Greatest Myths"** that have been perpetuated in our society about the nature of health and healing. These myths have derailed us, causing pain, confusion, and unnecessary suffering for far too long. It's time to flip them around once and for all. **The Truth is infinitely more empowering than we've ever been told.**

Have you ever:

- been told by a doctor: *"it's your age / it's your genes / it's incurable"* and *"there's nothing you can do about it?"*
- gotten sick or injured and felt like **your body has failed you**?
- been frustrated by an experience with a healthcare provider?

   Then Chapter 2 is especially written for you!

It's my intention that by the end of Part 1 "The Awakening," you'll feel excited and empowered with fresh new possibilities. You'll experience a renewed sense of **Freedom**. Freedom to enjoy life. Freedom to breathe. Freedom to return to your natural state of well-being.

Give yourself this freedom. You deserve it!

CHAPTER 1

Why "Eat Right and Exercise" is not the Key

"The obvious is that which is never seen until someone expresses it simply."

~ Kahlil Gibran ~

When you think about trying to get "healthy", what's the number one thing that comes to mind?

"To be healthy, you gotta Eat Right and Exercise," right? We've all heard that "Diet and Exercise" is the #1 key to our health. It's common knowledge. Of course it's true…

Or is it?

Let me ask you this: Do you know of someone that eats a very clean, healthy diet and works out regularly, yet they don't seem very healthy to you? Maybe they're still struggling with a chronic illness, despite the perfect diet and exercise?

On the flip side, do you know someone who doesn't eat the best diet or work out regularly, yet they're full of life, joy and vitality? Maybe they seem more vibrant than most people, even though they don't technically "Eat Right and Exercise?"

By now, I've asked this question to thousands of people. Everybody laughs and answers *"Yes."*

Surely we've all met people like that.

Is that confusing to you? It confused me for a very long time. I was told the importance of nutrition and exercise in all my training, in everything I had ever read, studied, or learned. They always say: "**To be healthy you must Eat Right and Exercise**", but if we look at people all around us, at some point we have to face the fact that this is **not necessarily true**!

The fact is, we all know people who "eat right and exercise" but are not very healthy. We all know people who don't eat the best diet, or don't workout regularly, but they seem vibrant and full of life. So what gives? What else is at play here?

Since I'm in Northern California, the land of the super-gungho-health-nuts, my patients tend to be extremely savvy. They've already read every popular book on nutrition and eat the perfect diet. They do yoga, pilates, and work out at the gym regularly. Many are competitive athletes. They could literally be professional nutritionists or fitness coaches with the amount they know. Yet they're still suffering from various chronic illnesses. Confused and frustrated, they come to my clinic for a professional consult. When I ask them to track their foods or exercise, I can find nothing major that needs to be changed.

For a long time, this baffled and frustrated me as a health practitioner, until I permitted myself to question the very obvious.

- What if... "diet and exercise" are **not** the most important keys?
- **Is it possible there are other lifestyle factors that are even more important?**

Once I dared to ask these questions, the floodgates opened, and a new understanding of health emerged. A classic "ships not seen" situation! It became clear that there are **many other lifestyle factors** that could be as important, or even more important, than Diet and Exercise!

As I supported my patients with lifestyle factors **beyond** Diet and Exercise, our clinical results skyrocketed.

This was the big-bang moment that created the SuperWellness universe.

Now let's be clear. I'm not saying that we should all start binge eating toxic junk foods and quit buying organic, or stop exercising and become couch potatoes. Surely Diet and Exercise do play a major role. But my patients have taught me that there are **other influences on our health that may be even more important than "Diet and Exercise."**

Case in point. A recent UK-based study was published in Nature magazine in Sept 2016 to understand the interactions between stress and healthy nutrition.

The study tracked blood levels of inflammation in two groups of women. One group ate a carefully designed "Anti-inflammatory" diet. The other ate the opposite: a carefully designed "Pro-inflammatory" diet. Participants' blood tests were taken to measure the levels of inflammation. The women were also given a survey of their stress levels.

(For readers who are medical research "nerds", it was a double-blind crossover study. They tracked C-reactive protein, serum amyloid A (SAA), intercellular adhesion molecule-1 (sICAM-1) and vascular cell adhesion molecule-1 (sVCAM-1) levels.)

Guess what they found? [3] [4]

They discovered that for participants who reported low stress, the results were exactly as expected. Subjects who ate the Pro-inflammatory diet showed increased inflammation. Those who ate the Anti-inflammatory diet showed decreased inflammation. All as expected.

Here's the kicker: when the women reported high levels of stress, it didn't matter what diet they ate! Both dietary groups had elevated levels of inflammation. So the study suggested that the **healthy diet may be beneficial only if we have stress-reduction as a foundation first**.

Is this fascinating? This suggests that 1) food and nutrition is still an important factor, but 2) it's secondary to our stress levels in influencing our health.

If stress has the ability to cancel out the positive effects of a healthy diet, then what other factors might also be at play? It's time for us to think more holistically about our lifestyle.

In Part II of this book, I'll share with you the key factors (H.E.A.L.T.H.) that synergize together to create true lasting health, based on all my years of clinical experience. But our formula for health will be incomplete without first addressing the underlying principles that tie them all together.

When we apply these principles, healthy living happens naturally and joyfully. Without these principles, our pursuit of healthy habits will always be an uphill battle requiring constant "willpower" or strict "discipline."

Willpower can only last so long, don't you agree? So let's find a more sustainable way.

THE CROWDING OUT METHOD

Have you heard of something called the "**Crowding Out**" **Method?**

This method was created by nutritionists who discovered that when we focus all our efforts on eliminating the "bad" junky foods, it backfires. The harder we try not to eat the "bad" stuff, the more we crave it! Have you experienced this too?

On the other hand, by nourishing ourselves with all the "good stuff," our cravings for the bad junky foods subsides. When we're fully satiated with the good stuff, it naturally "crowds out" the bad stuff.

Here's my big ah-ha moment:

"After coaching thousands of patients on their health and wellness, I discovered that the Crowding Out Method is a brilliant philosophy for all lifestyle habits, far beyond just food!"

When we enjoy more nourishing lifestyle activities, when we feel fulfilled on all levels, the "unhealthy" habits naturally fade away. They get "crowded out."

For example, when we focus on getting better sleep, spending time outdoors and in nature, getting enough sunshine, nurturing friendships, fun, and laughter, etc. many of the not-so-healthy habits can fade away. My patients tell me that their "stress-eating" or "emotional-eating" diminish naturally. From this state, they consistently show me that "Eat Right and

Exercise" can be a natural by-product of an overall nourishing lifestyle. We don't need to rely on willpower to achieve these results.

It's a more sane way to live. Don't you agree?

"But Dr. Edith, I heard that the food industry has made many food products highly addictive. We're addicted to the junk foods, the ice-cream, the cookies, and all that high-sugar foods. I've heard that sugar is as addictive as heroin! **Don't we need willpower to get over our addictions?"**

Well, it turns out that everything we thought we knew about addiction is inaccurate. Here's why.

A NEW UNDERSTANDING OF ADDICTION AND HABITS

We've all heard that Heroin (aka Diamorphine) is a highly addictive substance, right? But have you or a family member ever been hospitalized, where Diamorphine was prescribed to manage pain? If Heroin or Diamorphine is highly addictive, why is it that only a minority of patients who are prescribed it become addicted? How is it possible that the majority of people who are prescribed opioids do **not** get addicted? [5]

As it turns out, much of our popular understanding of addiction came from lab animal experiments in the early 20th century. Just like many of us, I have very mixed feelings about lab animal studies due to ethical considerations, but these studies on addiction are truly groundbreaking.

In early experiments, researchers would take a rat and put it in a simple cage with two water bottles. One bottle has regular water; the other has water laced with heroin. Nearly every time, the rats would choose the drugged water until it died of overdose. So the researchers concluded that heroin was highly addictive.

In the 1970s, a Professor of Psychology named Bruce Alexander noticed a strange characteristic in these experiments - the rat had nothing better to do in these cages! Of course it seems natural to choose the drugged water.

What if… you give the rat a better environment with more options? Professor Alexander decided to build a paradise-like rat park with everything that a rat might want – fun toys, tunnels, plenty of friends to play, mates to have sex, all that he could arrange for a wonderful environment. In "Rat Park," he gave them the same choice of regular water or drugged water.

The result? In his Rat Park, the rats rarely drank the drugged water! None of the rats ever used it compulsively, and not one rat ever overdosed!

There's a similar finding in humans too. During the Vietnam War, 20% of soldiers used heroin while at war. But surprisingly, when the veterans returned home to their loved ones, a study that followed them found that 95% stopped using heroin cold turkey and never became addicts!

Could it be that our environment, our social connections, and our access to "healthier" options is of enormous influence?

The information above is based on a fantastic YouTube video about Addiction, which I recommend highly! Look up "Addiction, Kurzgesagt - In a Nutshell." (The video cites a book called "Chasing the Scream" by Johann Hari. My gratitude to all for bringing forth such life-changing and empowering information.) [6]

"So Dr. Edith, is there no good reason for willpower or discipline then?"

What I've learned from 15 years observing thousands of patients is this: **Willpower and discipline is a short-term game. It can help us overcome the inertia of old habits, so that we can shift into a new pattern.** When we see initial success, we feel excited and encouraged! We open ourselves to a new set of possibilities and are then more likely to stay consistent with our new practices. But my patients have taught me that, in order to cultivate true vibrant health and lifelong well-being, **we need a much better long-term strategy than willpower.** We need a holistic lifestyle that's enjoyable and sustainable.

My patients have taught me that the key to long-term well-being is to create an environment and lifestyle that nourishes us on all levels. When we immerse ourselves in an environment that's conducive to the state that we seek, we drop many of the so-called "bad" habits naturally. Things like "healthy eating and exercise" can become a natural part of the upward spiral. And we don't need to rely solely on willpower.

JOURNAL ACTIVITY - BEYOND "EAT RIGHT AND EXERCISE"

Now let's hear what you think! How can you create a lifestyle that nurtures your wellness, beyond "Eat Right and Exercise?" Make it more fun by sharing these questions with friends and family. There's so much we can learn from one another.

- **Think of the people you know who don't eat very healthy** or work out regularly, yet they're vibrant, healthy and full of life. What's their secret? What is it about their lifestyle that keeps them so vibrant and healthy? If you don't know, ask them!

- **Now think of your own life.** What are some non-food, non-exercise ways to <u>nourish your physical body</u>?

- What are some non-food, non-exercise ways to <u>nourish your mind</u>?

- What about <u>your emotions</u>? What are non-food, non-exercise practices that make you feel emotionally balanced, connected, and joyful?

- Finally, what activities are most <u>nourishing to your soul</u>? What keeps you inspired? What makes your heart and soul sing that has nothing to do "Eat-Right-and-Exercise?"

In our SuperWellness classes, the most popular answers include:

Sunshine, Sleep, Nature-time, Outdoors, Breathing, Music, Dancing, Hugs, Intimacy, Laughter, Comedy, Quality Time w/ Friends & Family, Community, Volunteer Service, Meditation, Turning Off Phones and Digital Devices, more Down-time to Relax, Chillout and Do Nothing.

As you look through your answers to the questions above, what are you most "hungry" for right now? What calls to you the most?

In SuperWellness, many participants are moved to tears at the recognition that these are the true "Essential Nutrients" for a human being to thrive. Many of us have been chronically "malnourished" in these areas for far too long.

When we learn how to truly nourish ourselves on all levels: body, mind, emotions, and soul, we may find that old unhealthy habits fade away gently. Healthier eating and movement can be a natural part of the overall healthy spiral, without so much willpower or discipline.

If you haven't already, please claim your Chapter 1 book bonuses at: www.SuperWellness.com/BookBonuses/ . Enjoy a video where we explore more ideas around nourishing activities that are beyond diet and exercise.

Thousands of clients and patients have shared with me how **liberating** it feels to learn that "Diet and Exercise" is not the "end all and be all" of our health. **It's only one of many factors** that synergize together to create our sense of well-being.

In this new world of SuperWellness, we expand far beyond the "Diet and Exercise" paradigm. We can enjoy a lifestyle that's fun, joyful, and requires zero deprivation. I hope it feels exciting and empowering as you open yourself to these new possibilities!

Being the open-minded person that you are, at this moment, you may be thinking:

"Wow, if 'Eat Right and Exercise' is not the #1 key to health, then what else have I been taught that may not be true?"

In the next chapter, we'll bust the **Five Greatest Myths** that have derailed us for far too long. It's the truth that will empower us to enjoy vibrant health and lifelong well-being.

CHAPTER 2

The Five Greatest Myths that Derail Us from Our Health

"The Key to Wisdom is this - constant and frequent questioning. For by doubting we're led to the question. By questioning we're led to the truth."

~ Peter Abelard ~

HOW I CAME TO QUESTION EVERYTHING

I n 2003, I was in the middle of a Qigong class guided by a great teacher from my Chinese Medicine school. For someone interested in meditation, living in Northern California was like being a kid in the candy store. I had tried many forms of meditation, but like most people I found it difficult to get still and quiet my mind... until I experienced Qigong.

Qigong is a 5000-year-old meditation and breathwork practice from China, where we weave together three key elements: 1) a conscious intention, 2) a breathing technique, and 3) directing the flow of energy in the body. This three-pronged approach of Qigong helped me to finally quiet my monkey-mind and find the stillness that is taught in all the meditative traditions. I loved my Qigong classes and always felt a sense of calm and well-being from the practices.

But nothing could have prepared me for what happened next.

On this particular day in 2003, I dropped so deeply into meditation that suddenly, something extraordinary happened. One moment, I was sitting peacefully following a guided breathing, visualization, and meditation practice. Then the next moment...

I experienced myself bursting...

Bursting into trillions of pieces of Love and Light.

I experienced myself the size of the entire cosmos.

No more physical body. No time. No space.

The feeling was so intensely blissful, so beautiful, so filled with love... I had no reference point for anything like this in my earthly life.

All I knew was that - **I was Home.**

All I knew was that - **this is our natural state.**

Every question I ever had was answered. There were no more questions. Just complete and utter contentment.

Pure light.

Pure love.

Pure peace.

I knew with every fiber of my being that I was Home, that this is our true natural state.

Eventually a thought came in, that maybe I (or "it" or "this") should return to the physical body.

When I ("it") did return to the physical, there were no words. Just avalanches of tears. Tears of joy and immense gratitude at the remembrance of my true natural state. Also tears of sorrow for leaving that pure state of light, spirit, and energy. It felt intensely awkward to squeeze such enormous love and light back into this world of density and physical form.

Many people would say: *"Wow. You had a sudden awakening; an out-of-body enlightenment experience. How lucky!"*

For me at the time, it didn't feel so lucky. After the awakening experience, my intuition skyrocketed, and I became acutely sensitive to all the pains and suffering around me. It often felt overwhelming, painful, and confusing. I began to see all the density and distortions of our world from a fresh new perspective. With this new sensitivity, much of how we humans have organized our society (and life) was no longer acceptable to me.

I continued to function normally on the outside. But on the inside, I became a different person overnight.

On the one hand, there was great comfort in knowing that this state of bliss, joy, peace, and love is our true nature. I felt totally at home, whole and complete in this state of meditation. The experience was more real than anything I had ever experienced in our world of physical form. So I became addicted to meditation in order to return to this peaceful state. I knew in my heart and soul that the conflicts, wars, illness, and suffering in our world would cease to exist if we could all learn how to anchor this peaceful and loving state into our world.

On the other hand, the fact remains that here in our physical world, we do have conflict. We do have war. We do have much pain, illness, and suffering.

This created an inner tension within my being, and I couldn't help but question everything. The enhanced intuition and acute sensitivity to all the pain and suffering around me meant that there was no escape from it. At times, this heightened sensitivity felt like a painful curse. Today, I see it as the greatest gift.

I developed a ferocious appetite for new ways of seeing our world - reading thousands of books on personal growth, spirituality, the meaning of life, the nature of healing, illness, and suffering, and the interaction between mind-body-spirit. I was especially drawn to others who also had these sudden mystical awakenings or so-called "Near Death Experiences" (NDEs), especially those who had spontaneous healing experiences.

Beyond my studies in school and my apprenticeship with Dr. Fu, I traveled around the world learning from teachers, healers, and shamans, seeking truth. **I questioned everything.** I dove into deep meditation, contemplation, and inquiry practices. I explored countless holistic healing modalities. There was no stopping until my heart and soul could find answers that were in harmony with that pure state of love, peace, and joy I experienced on that incredible day in 2003.

Gradually over time, the puzzle pieces started coming together, and I have very good news for you!

I discovered that we live in unprecedented times of massive awakenings across the planet. Much of this awakening is triggered by the pace of intense and rapid changes in our world, and assisted by the easy access to inspiring and empowering information through technology and the internet. The old and unsustainable paradigms are breaking down, while conscious new ways of living are anchoring in.

The tools are now available for us to create a life that's aligned with our highest selves - a life that is joyful, fulfilling, authentic, healthy, and filled with love.

I've also discovered that, because of greed and profits, some forces at work in our world have perpetuated disempowering myths that keep us from our true limitless nature. Generation after generation, we've been taught a set of false beliefs that have actually derailed us from our joy, health, and well-being.

To put it bluntly, keeping us ignorant and disempowered is good for industry profits, and that's why many of these false myths have been perpetuated for so long.

The good news is that we now have a choice. We can learn the truth. We do not need to buy into these limiting beliefs any longer.

It is my great honor and privilege to share with you these life-changing discoveries. Together, let's question the old limiting paradigm and turn the greatest myths upside down. Let's discover the truth that can set us Free.

THE FIVE GREATEST MYTHS

When it comes to our health, I've discovered that there are FIVE GREAT MYTHS that have been perpetrated in our society that patients and doctors alike have been falsely educated into believing. All too often, these Five Myths have kept us feeling frustrated, disempowered, and even hopeless about our health. Rather than helping us, they have actually been derailing us from our health.

Not long ago, I was also a "believer" of these big myths too. But in my heart, I knew there had to be a way out of the hopelessness and despair. One by one I began to challenge these beliefs. It turns out, the truth is far more hopeful and empowering than we ever imagined!

Ready? Let's dive in.

Myth #1: *"Whose job is it to take care of our Health? It's our Doctor's job, of course!"*

We live in a society where we outsource everything these days, including our health. We've been taught to believe it's the responsibility of doctors, not our own, to take care of our health. Our education system emphasizes academics like math, science, history, and English, but the most important subject of all - our Health - gets little attention.

If we're fortunate enough to have a health class, we may be taught the basic food groups, "saying no to drugs," or preventing pregnancy and STDs. We learn almost nothing about a truly healthy lifestyle.

Unless we grew up playing sports, most of us have not cultivated our body awareness or body confidence. Our culture encourages us to focus on outside looks (*"I want six-pack abs."* or *"Can I fit into those skinny jeans?"*), but we rarely pay attention to how our body feels on the <u>inside</u>. The fact is, most of us don't think very deeply about our health until our body breaks down in a serious or debilitating way.

We've come to believe that "health care" is our doctor's job, not our own.

Here's the issue: How long are your average doctor's visits? And how many times a year?

Most people tell me: About 15 minutes? Maybe once or twice a year?

I know many great doctors whom I admire deeply. They are all brilliant people with the best hearts. But with these short visits, and the economics of medicine today (at least here in the U.S.), it has become the standard-of-care for doctors to prescribe a pill that manages symptoms only. It's virtually impossible for our good-hearted doctors to support patients in cultivating a truly healthy lifestyle and educating them on the root cause of disease.

Another aspect which may be well-known to some readers, but a total shocker to others is the amount of time that most conventionally trained Medical Doctors are given to study Nutrition and Lifestyle.

Do you know how much Nutrition and Lifestyle training most MDs receive?

It turns out, on average, U.S. Medical Schools spend only 19.6 hours on nutrition and lifestyle education. That's less than one semester total! [7] [8] Since you're reading this book on wellness, the chances are very high that you may know more about healthy lifestyle than many conventionally trained doctors in this country. No wonder our system is so great in the areas of acute traumas, emergency medicine, and advanced diagnostics, yet it's so poor at resolving chronic conditions that are largely lifestyle-related.

It's not our doctor's fault. The basic structure of medical school training was put into place back in the 1920s, before lifestyle-related chronic diseases became such a huge epidemic in our society. Many doctors today believe they should learn more about healthy lifestyle and true prevention and would like to support their patients in this. But unfortunately, our standard-of-care medical system makes it challenging for doctors to fill the huge gap between managing symptoms with pharmaceutical drugs and supporting patients on creating a healthy lifestyle.

Given how rushed the average doctor's visits are, and the lack of education that most conventional MDs are given in the area of healthy lifestyle, it's virtually impossible for most doctors to truly support us in healthy living.

So let's turn this Myth upside-down. Rather than making it our doctor's job to take care of our health, let's recognize the truth. It's <u>our</u> job!

It's each of our jobs to take beautiful care of our health and personal well-being! Instead of those 10-15 minute appointments, you get to be with yourself 24 x 7, 365 days a year, for the rest of your life. When it comes to a healthy lifestyle that works for you, you have the power to know yourself far better than any doctor could. Isn't that true?

Of course, **it's still critically important to consult doctors for expert opinions, diagnostics, evaluation, and appropriate treatment**. Our doctors didn't go through seven to ten-plus years of medical training for nothing! Their expertise is priceless and oftentimes lifesaving. Plus, there are now many courageous and pioneering doctors stepping outside the conventional system to offer Functional Medicine consultations with more holistic nutrient-based therapies. (*If you're one such pioneering doctor reading this book, I salute you!*) It's also valuable to consult with professional wellness coaches, nutritionists, movement therapists, and more. At the end of the day, let's remember that **you're the boss**! All your doctors and professional experts out there are advisors working for you.

In other words, you are always the CEO of your life. All the professional practitioners are here to work for you. You're the boss. Now, how's that for self-empowerment?

Truth #1: When it comes to your health, **<u>you</u>** are the boss. You have the power to know yourself better than anyone else. Your doctor is simply here to support you. So let's put you back in the driver's seat of your life again.

"You da boss." Myth #1 - busted.

Myth #2: *"Your condition is incurable; there's nothing you can do about it."..."It's all in your genes, and there's nothing you can do about it."*

Have you ever been frustrated or felt hopeless, because a doctor said: *"There's no cure for this. There's nothing you can do about it."* or *"It's all in your genes. There's nothing you can do about it?"*

I hope not. But in my experience, far too many people who struggle with chronic health conditions have been left feeling frustrated, angry, and hopeless, because a doctor says *"There's no cure. There's nothing you can do about it."*

But let's remember, our conventional Western medical doctors are primarily trained in pharmaceutical drugs and surgical procedures, yet these are far from being the only options out there. So when a conventional doctor says "there's no cure," it really means:

"As far as I'm aware, there is no known cure for your condition <u>within the realms of pharmaceutical drugs or surgical procedures</u>. Because my scope of training is focused on drugs and surgery, your condition may be beyond my training. So you might like to look into other alternatives."

Once we realize this, it's actually very good news! Because we can direct our attention towards researching options - beyond conventional drugs and surgery. For many of our modern chronic health conditions, there is an explosion of research supporting the power of holistic approaches like mind-body medicine, nutrition, lifestyle, acupuncture, herbal medicine, osteopathy, chiropractic, breathwork, meditation and mindfulness, qigong, yoga, heat/light/sound/energy medicines, and more. This is very exciting!

This book does not diagnose, treat, or advise on any medical conditions, nor do we claim any "cures." But I can share that amongst my natural/holistic medicine colleagues, it's not uncommon to see patients recover from so-called "incurable" or mysterious conditions like eczema, allergies, asthma, IBS, rheumatoid arthritis, thyroid conditions, chronic pain and inflammatory conditions, hormonal irregularities, etc.. When we take a holistic approach, reduce stress, bring balance and alignment back to the system, optimize our nutrition and lifestyle, etc., many chronic conditions can improve as a side-effect.

You might be saying:

"Ok Dr. Edith. But what about our genes? Aren't genes fixed? Don't they determine our health?"

Oh I'm so glad you asked! Yes, we used to think that genes were fixed. But in the past few decades, the **science of epigenetics** is showing us more and more how we can influence our genetic expression through healthy lifestyle, nutrition, environment, stress, thoughts, beliefs, and emotions. A full discussion of epigenetics is beyond the scope of this chapter, but I invite you to research the pioneering work of Dr. Bruce Lipton, author of *"The Biology of Belief."*

The field of epigenetics is still relatively new, but we now have clear scientific evidence that lifestyle factors have powerful influence on our genetic expression.[9]

What an amazing time in which we live!

In the past, we also thought that our brains were doomed to decline as we age. But over the past 30 years, the discovery of "neuroplasticity" has demonstrated that our brains are constantly rewiring, learning, and adapting throughout our entire lives. Similarly, the science of epigenetics has demonstrated that our genes can be switched on and off. They are influenced by our thoughts, emotions, environmental factors, nutrition and more.

So today, we can no longer say *"It's all in your genes, so there's nothing you can do about it."* Such a statement is simply not true anymore.

Myth #2 busted!

Truth #2a: There are <u>many</u> alternative options, outside of drugs or surgery, that are worthy of consideration.

Truth #2b: The science of epigenetics shows that we can influence our gene expression through lifestyle, nutrition, environmental factors, thoughts, beliefs, emotions, and more.

Myth #3: *"The best solutions for our health are also the most expensive ones."*

This is perhaps the most compelling reason why our world needs SuperWellness. Here in the U.S., we have by far the most expensive healthcare. In 2016, U.S. national medical care expenditure reached $3.35 trillion; that's an average of $10,345 per person![10] Yet we're consistently the sickest country amongst modern industrialized nations.[11] It has become the norm in our society to be overweight, stressed out, tired, unhealthy, and depressed.

It's time to question this myth that "expensive is better," don't you agree?

In politics, we often hear debates about how to pay for the increasing costs of healthcare. Yet we never seem to discuss the biggest issues - Why is healthcare so darn expensive? And why are we getting sicker and sicker as a country?

Isn't it time to question the economics of our so-called "health"care, which many of us now call the "sick"care system?

The truth is, over my last 15 years supporting the healing programs of thousands of patients, we've discovered that most of our patients suffer from modern stress or lifestyle-related conditions. While there is a critical and indispensable role that modern medicine must play, especially in the areas of medical diagnostics and urgent life-threatening conditions, the truth is that many of our chronic health conditions are rooted in very simple lifestyle factors. Addressing these lifestyle factors does not have to be so complex or expensive!

In fact, we've found over and over that some of the most powerful self-care strategies are simple and free!

"Dr. E, if there are such great simple and free tools, why don't we ever hear about these?"

I believe it comes down to simple economics. Because these lifestyle practices cannot be patented, industries cannot make profits off of them. So as a result, they haven't gotten the airtime they deserve! We're inundated with TV ads for pharmaceutical drugs because they are so profitable. But there are no profits to fund advertisements for self-care practices like - breathwork, mindfulness, sunshine, sleep, time in nature, unhooking from your devices, and other such simple and potent health enhancing strategies.

So, unwittingly, we've allowed industries to narrow our focus towards expensive drugs that generate the highest profits. They have shifted our attention away from the many powerful self-care tools that are inexpensive and abundantly available to every human being.

At the end of the day, you empowering yourself with simple and free lifestyle practices is not profitable for any industries. That's the bottom line.

Of course, you and I both know that self-care practices like deep breathing feels great, right? It's totally common-sense. But is it common practice? That's the question. Until we put these simple tools back into consistent practice, we cannot believe how powerful they can be. So let's make a commitment together. **Let's put common-sense back into practice and see what happens. This is the secret sauce of SuperWellness.**

One particularly potent example I invite you to explore is the Wim Hof Method. If you haven't heard of Wim Hof until now, please do an online search for the VICE documentary on Wim Hof. By the end of the documentary, you'll be leaping out of your chair, blown away by the power of simple breathing practice. (For readers who are interested in learning the Wim Hof Method, visit www.wimhofmethod.com .)

SuperWellness is all about these types of free, simple, and empowering ninja-tools. This book contains a treasure trove of such tools waiting for you!

So are you ready to turn this "expensive is better" myth upside-down?

Truth #3: Some of the most potent and powerful healing tools are also simple, free, and abundantly available! Because they can't be patented and industries can't make money off of them, they're not getting the airtime they deserve. So it's up to each of us to educate and empower ourselves.

Myth #3, busted.

Myth #4: *"The body, mind, emotions, and spirit are all separate. Some conditions are just 'all in your head'."*

I hope nobody has said this to you. But sadly, far too many of my patients have told me their health concerns went unacknowledged by a medical practitioner at some point, saying: *"Your condition is all in your head."* This is especially common amongst patients that have poorly understood conditions such as Chronic Fatigue or Fibromyalgia.

In the old "sick-care" paradigm, we were often told that some conditions are only in the body, some are in our mind, and some are emotional, as if these are all mutually exclusive.

The truth is, our body, mind, emotions, and spirit are intimately connected and cannot be truly separated.

For example:

Have you ever eaten food that didn't sit well in your stomach? What about foods to which you are sensitive or allergic? Traditionally, we think of eating and digesting food as a physical or physiological activity. But have you noticed how irritable you feel when you eat the wrong foods? Maybe you feel mentally unclear or foggy-headed. Maybe you get more impatient with your spouse or kids. Maybe you experience mood changes. Have you noticed it's also more difficult to focus, or to meditate and get calm and still?

On the flipside, have you noticed when you eat a more clean and healthy diet that your mind is more clear and stable?

Here's another example:

Let's say you start your day feeling good. Then suddenly you hear some bad news that triggers a lot of emotional stress. Instantly your body gets tense, tight, and even painful. Perhaps you lose your appetite and notice nausea or digestive upset, and you sleep poorly that night. We've all experienced how mental and emotional stress can create a physical manifestation. On the other hand, have you noticed that when you're on vacation and feeling relaxed, that many physical discomforts can disappear?

From these examples, we can see how the body influences the mind, and the mind influences the body.

What about the spiritual dimension? We all know people in our communities that may not have the most healthy lifestyle on the surface. Maybe they don't eat the perfect diet or exercise. But they live a passionate, soulful, and purposeful life, and they seem deeply fulfilled. They radiate a contagious joyful energy and have unstoppable energy and stamina. Everybody wonders how this is possible. Do you know someone like this?

From these examples, we can see that it's not possible to separate body, mind, emotions, and spirit. Some lifestyle practices influence one aspect more directly than another. But ultimately, what benefits one level will also support all the others.

So rather than separating body, mind, emotions, and spirit, let us take a more holistic and integrated approach. Let's choose to take beautiful care of all aspects of our being - body-mind-emotions-spirit. Let's honor the wholeness of our entire human experience. This is the SuperWellness way.

Truth #4: The Body, Mind, Emotions, and Spirit are all intimately connected and cannot be truly separated. It takes a holistic integrated approach to create a thriving human being.

Myth #4 - Busted.

Myth #5: *"Getting sick/injured is always a bad thing. I don't ever want to get sick or injured."*

Have you ever had the experience where you got sick or injured, and you said to yourself: *"Darn it, body! I don't have time for this!"* and you felt like your body was failing you?

Surely we've all been there. At times like this, it's easy to feel frustrated at the situation. We may feel like our body has failed us. I've been there too.

Over the years, as I've deepened my study of human physiology, I've come to see that this frustration actually stems from a great misunderstanding about how our body works.

The truth is, **our human body is a masterpiece.** It is a miraculous and elegant bio-computer, always responding intelligently and doing its best to recover from every stressor of life. **Our body is powerful, adaptive, and designed to heal.**

For example, when you catch a cold or flu, did you know that your body is creating a cascade of intelligent immune responses that science has yet to fully understand? Your body generates the precise fever to kill the pathogen, but not to kill your healthy cells. Your body may produce mucus to push out the pathogen and protect it from being invaded any further. You may feel tired or groggy, so that you will take a much needed rest. You may even lose your appetite, because periodic "Intermittent Fasting" allows the body to devote its energy and resources to healing. Most importantly, if you respect the body's need to rest and recover, you'll develop lifelong immunity.

Is this not a miracle?

So the next time we get sick, perhaps a more fitting response could be:

"Wow! Thank you, body! Thank you for mounting the perfect immune response. I will listen to your needs and take good care so we can recover faster. I'm happy to give you the rest and recovery you need, so that we can become immune to this virus for the rest of our life. Thank you, body, for responding so elegantly and healing so quickly! I am so grateful for this body."

I believe this would be a much more correct and appropriate response, based on a truer understanding of human physiology, honoring this miracle of our body-temple, don't you agree?

In fact, the more deeply we study our human experience, we may discover that every illness or injury can be an opportunity to cultivate strength, wisdom, and growth. Every experience can be a blessing in disguise.

If you're an athlete, you can relate to this.

When top athletes come into our clinic for treatments, we are always inspired by the positive attitude that they bring. Rather than feeling stuck, victimized, or frustrated by the injury, the most successful athletes seem to use their injury as an opportunity to learn and grow. Not only do they come in for their therapeutic treatments, they always look for ways to improve their biomechanics, adjust their equipment, or discuss with their coach(es) how to optimize the training program to avoid future injury. They have the attitude of a student, always learning and growing from each experience.

Not only do these athletes heal quickly from the injury, they also learn something about themselves that empowers them to be fitter, stronger, faster, and smarter for the rest of their athletic career. Rather than being "set back" by the injury, their performance often skyrockets.

In this way, the challenge of an illness or injury can turn into a great gift.

Perhaps the most moving of all is the experience of serving patients through a major health crisis. Have you ever supported a friend or family member through a very serious illness?

I am so moved by how, in the face of a serious medical diagnosis, our patients go into a state of deep soul-searching. Those of you who are health practitioners, or caretakers, surely you've witnessed this too. I think we can all agree: this is one of the most humbling and heart-opening experiences for us as practitioners and caretakers.

When we know that our time on earth may be limited, we become so much more present, aware, and in many ways even more "alive" than ever before. No longer do we engage in superficial, petty, or meaningless activities or conversations. We treasure each and every opportunity to express our love and gratitude for one another. We become more clear, present, and connected as human beings. We embrace each and every moment.

While nobody wishes or plans to have a serious illness, my patients have taught me how a major health crisis can be an opportunity to awaken, re-align, and clarify what truly matters in life. I am often moved to tears thinking of my patients who have been my greatest teachers in this realm.

Sometimes this clarity creates profound ripple effects that uncover a new way of engaging with every aspect of life. From this clarity, we may find deep healing on all levels - body, mind, emotions, and spirit. From this state, we may have a brand new relationship with life.

A major health crisis can have this kind of power, if we can open our hearts to it.

Through the journey of illness and injuries, my patients have taught me the most important lessons in life - lessons that no textbooks could ever teach. They've taught me what it means to be truly alive. They've taught me about humility, courage, and love.

Most of all, they've taught me to embrace life's challenges, to learn and grow from every experience, and to treasure every moment as a precious gift.

So with humility and a tender heart, let's turn this Myth #5 upside down.

Truth #5: Life is full of surprises. While we would never plan to become sick or injured, sometimes health challenges can be a great blessing in disguise, if we can open our hearts to it. Within every challenge lies an opportunity for learning and growth.

Myth #5 - busted.

If you're like most of us, these Five Great Myths have been a source of much frustration when dealing with challenges in our health and healing. I hope that busting these myths feels liberating and empowering!

I invite you to discuss and debate these five myths with your friends and family. For easy reference, below is a summary of the Five Myths and their Truths.

SUMMARY OF THE FIVE GREAT MYTHS

Myth #1: "Whose job is it to take care of our Health? It's our Doctor's job, of course!"

Truth #1: Actually, when it comes to your health, <u>you</u> are the boss! You have the power to know yourself better than anyone else. Your doctor is simply here to support you. So let's put you back in the driver's seat of your life again.

Myth #2: "Your condition is incurable; there's nothing you can do about it."..."It's all in your genes and there's nothing you can do about it."

Truth #2a: There are <u>many</u> alternative options worthy of consideration, outside of drugs or surgery.

Truth #2b: The science of epigenetics shows that we can influence our gene expression through lifestyle, nutrition, environmental factors, thoughts, beliefs, emotions, and more.

Myth #3: "The best solutions for our health are also the most expensive ones."

Truth #3: Many of the most potent and powerful healing tools are also simple, free, and abundantly available! Because they can't be patented and industries can't make money off of them, they're not getting the airtime they deserve. So it's up to each of us to educate and empower ourselves.

Myth #4: "The body, mind, emotions, and spirit are all separate. They're addressed separately. Some conditions are just 'all in your head.'"

Truth #4: The Body, Mind, Emotions, and Spirit are all intimately connected and cannot be truly separated.

Myth #5: "Getting sick/injured is always a bad thing. I don't ever want to get sick or injured."

Truth #5: Life is full of surprises. While we would never plan to become sick or injured, sometimes health challenges can be a great blessing in disguise, if we can open our hearts to it. Within every challenge lies an opportunity for learning and growth.

As we complete our journey of Part I "The Awakening," I want to congratulate and honor you for your commitment to self-empowerment and self-discovery.

Did you know? Statistics show that many people love to buy non-fiction how-to books, but less than 10% actually read past chapter one? The fact that you're still here reading these words says something about your level of commitment and mastery. Please take a moment to pat yourself on the back, my friend!

JOURNAL ACTIVITY - THE FIVE GREAT MYTHS

Now let's celebrate and integrate with these questions:

- What was your favorite game-changing insight from this chapter on the Five Greatest myths?

- What idea surprised you the most in the book so far?

- How has the book shifted your attitude towards your health thus far?

Please claim your book bonuses at:

www.SuperWellness.com/BookBonuses/

Share your insights with our online SuperWellness community, so that we may all learn and grow together.

At this point, you may be thinking:

"This all sounds wonderful. But what now? How do I go about taking charge of my health? Give me the tools that really work."

Part I was called "The Awakening" because we stepped into this exciting world of new possibilities. But these concepts have no power until we put them into action.

So without further ado, I invite you into Part II "The Recalibration," where we get practical with the Six Dimensions of H.E.A.L.T.H..

When the Six Dimensions of H.E.A.L.T.H. are activated, we can experience joy, health, and well-being as a natural byproduct. Without the holistic foundation, our journey of health will always be a struggle.

You'll learn the simple but profound keys to your health that you can put into action right away. I will share with you a treasure-trove of potent self-care tools that truly work, tools that have been carefully curated over my last 15 years.

Ready to experience SuperWellness for yourself? Let's go.

PART II: THE RECALIBRATION

"You are the master of your destiny.
You can influence, direct and control your
own environment. You can make your life
what you want it to be."

~ Napolean Hill ~

W elcome to Part II! We're about to take a wild and beautiful journey into this bold new world called SuperWellness.

In the previous chapters, we busted the old myths and paradigms that have limited us, creating unnecessary frustration, pain, and suffering for far too long.

Now comes the exciting part: activating YOUR SuperWellness!

In Part II "The Recalibration," you'll experience:

- why getting healthy can be fun, joyful and requires zero deprivation.
- the most powerful self-care tools that are also free, simple, and abundantly available.
- how you can **become stress-free, get the best sleep, lose those pesky pounds without dieting, heal faster, look radiant, have amazing energy, and enjoy more quality time with your friends, family, and kids.**
- getting back in the driver's seat of your health again as "Your Own Best Healer." While you'll continue to take full advantage of professionals as your expert advisors and support team, you've taken back the power as boss and CEO of your own life.

Together, let's explore the Six Key Dimensions of SuperWellness - H.E.A.L.T.H..

When the six keys of H.E.A.L.T.H. are in place, we can experience sustained levels of joy, health, and well-being as a natural byproduct. Without the holistic foundation, our journey of health will always be a struggle.

We'll weave together cutting edge science, ancient wisdom, and all my years of clinical experience as we step into this new world of SuperWellness. Be amazed, as you discover how and why health and wellness is your natural state.

Success Tip: The ideas in this section are powerful, but good ideas are useless without implementation. To get the most out of this book, I invite you to take your time to digest each chapter and experience the recommended activities. Don't be fooled by the apparent simplicity of these tools. The results will amaze you. But you won't know their true power unless you put them into practice. The life-changing magic only happens with their implementation. Ready? Let's ride!

CHAPTER 3

'H' is for Coming Home

"Knowing others is intelligence; knowing yourself is true wisdom. Mastering others is strength; mastering yourself is true power."

~ Dao De Jing, Chapter 33 ~

THE SEARCH FOR MINDFULNESS

Recently, I was invited to Reddit's headquarters to speak with their employees about Wellness. The room was filled with young, smart go-getters, and the Reddit panel moderator asked me: *"Dr. Edith, can you talk about Mindfulness? What is Mindfulness?"*

Mindfulness has become quite the buzzword in recent years, especially here in Silicon Valley. It seems we've been hearing "mindfulness" attached to everything in self-help, personal development, and corporate training. Some critics say that it's become so commercialized and overused that many have lost the true essence of its practice. Some have even started calling this trend *"McMindfulness."* [12]

Sometimes you just have to laugh. (*"Would you like a side of fries with your McMindfulness?"*) Our world has such a tendency to over-complicate things in an effort to make them trendy, doesn't it? Mindfulness is one of these things. We've been taught to think that the more complex an idea is, the more advanced it must be. Even better if there's an app for it, right?

The truth is - mindfulness is very, very simple.

Mindfulness = coming Home to ourselves.

Mindfulness means being present, aware, and coming home. It's a practical first step in any situation. From this state, wisdom and right action arises naturally.

It's really that simple.

And we don't need an app for it, or decades of advanced ninja training.

So when the panel moderator at Reddit asked about Mindfulness, I was excited to share this beautiful truth with them.

To demonstrate its simplicity, I asked the Reddit employees a few questions. I invite you to also try this out for yourself, and test it with your friends too!

*"Quick question for everybody. Please raise your hand if you know **your phone's battery level** to the nearest 10% without looking at it right now. Is it at 30-40%? Is it 40-50%? Is it 60-70%? Do you know your phone's battery level?"* I asked.

Nearly every person raised their hand. We all know our phones so well. In fact, a recent study showed that the average smartphone user checks their phone 150x each day! [13]

*"Ok great! Now tell me. What's **your body's energy level on a scale of 10**, right now? How's your energy? Scale of 10."*

The audience looked stunned. Taken off guard. Nobody raised their hand.

*"Is that crazy? **How is it that we know more about the energy state of our phones, than the energy state of our own bodies?"** I said.

"Isn't it nuts that we know our phones better than our own bodies?"

Laughter and embarrassment wafted through the room. Chuckle. Chuckle.

So I invited everyone to take three deep breaths. *"Breathe in… let it out… In… Out… Get still. Drop in. Let's become aware of our own bodies again. As we breathe, let's drop in and scan the body."*

"Now that we're back in our bodies, can you feel into it? At this moment, what's your Energy on a scale of 10?"

I surveyed the audience; it was beautiful. Everyone was going within and reconnecting with themselves again. Most people said they were about 2/3/4 out of 10 in their energy. Good! This is the beginning of Mindfulness. It can be this simple!

So I asked the group: *"If it were your phone running on 30% charge, would you not be thinking about charging it back up soon? When it comes to your body's energy level, what do you do to quickly recharge in the middle of the day?"*

Do you have a morning energizer practice? A mid-day energizer practice?

Next I invited everyone in the Reddit audience to go from seated to standing. Standing nice and tall, with good postural alignment. *"Now let's scan your energy. Did it go from a 2-4, up to a 5-6 just from changing your body posture?"*

This type of mindful awareness is so simple. It's practical. And it's life-changing.

We just need to put it back into practice.

Next we shared a Deep Breathing and five-minute Qigong movement exercise. *Boom!* The energy of the room shifted massively! Within ten minutes, when I surveyed the room again, everybody declared their energy level went up to a 9 or 10 on a scale of 10!

Later in this chapter, we'll explore the power of Breathwork. I'll show you the exact same **Breathing and Qigong movement practice** that lifted the Reddit group's energy so dramatically, so that you can experience it for yourself.

THE FIRST 'H' OF H.E.A.L.T.H.

As you know, our Six Keys of SuperWellness has a simple acronym H.E.A.L.T.H..

The first 'H' is for <u>coming Home to ourselves</u>, **tapping into our inner wisdom, and returning to our natural state of well-being.**

In previous chapters, we began the journey of "Coming Home" by remembering that we're each the "boss" of our own lives. Now let's go much deeper. To be an effective boss, we must have Clarity.

So let's start with the most fundamental question: "What is Health?"

WHAT'S YOUR DEFINITION OF HEALTH, BOSS?

We all want to be healthy. But what is Health? More importantly, what is **your** personal definition of health?

Since the first SuperWellness class, we've been blessed to share this program with many brilliant and open-minded doctors, MDs, PhDs, researchers, nurses and health professionals. Time and time again, the conventionally trained doctors tell us they were most blown away by this first question in class #1.

"What is your definition of Health?"

When I ask this question in class, participants who are conventionally trained medical professionals are often the most surprised. Our MD friends tell us that in their 7 to 10+ years of medical training, despite being labeled a "Health" practitioner, their training never truly explored this fundamental question: What is Health?

Our brilliant doctors have undergone tens of thousands of hours in advanced and intense training. They have expert understanding in the mechanism of dis-ease, all the ways in which the body breaks down and falls ill, the pharmacology, drugs, surgery, important emergency protocols and life-saving procedures, and many other highly advanced specialty topics.

But what about Health & Healing? What is true health? How does healing work?

Is it any wonder that we have a mainstream medical system that's so great at "sick"care, but so poor at true "health"care?

On the first day of our SuperWellness class, when I ask "What is your definition of Health", participants from all walks of life share beautiful wisdom:

- *"Health is a state of dynamic balance, integration, and wholeness."*
- *"Health is the optimal functioning of all aspects of my being - body, mind, emotions, and spirit."*
- *"Health is resilience and adaptability to the stressors of life."*
- *"Health is the feeling of connection and oneness."*
- *"Health is living a life of joy and fulfillment, and having the sense of overall well-being."*
- *"Health is the ability to be fully present, to enjoy life, to live confidently without being distracted by physical limitations or fear of future illness or injury."*
- *"Health is the freedom to live my life to the fullest."*

"As an MD, I have long recognized that western medicine defines health as the absence of detectable disease, which is a far cry from TRUE wellness. This course demonstrated concrete steps to effectively improve my health that I never would have embarked upon without Dr. Edith's guidance and expertise. Highly recommended!"

~ Dr. S. Lee, MD

As part of this discussion, our conventionally trained MD friends often lament that **they were trained to view Health as the mere *"absence of illness or disease."*** But of course, as wise human beings with a depth of personal experience, they also feel that true Health is so much more beautiful and elegant than just "the absence of disease."

To prove it, let me ask you another important question:

"Does a Healthy person ever get sick or injured?"

"Yes of course", you say.

So I ask you: *"Is it true that a Healthy person will **never** get sick? Never get injured?"*

"Of course not!"

This begs the question: ***"How does a Healthy person respond to illness/injury, in a way that is different from an unhealthy or sickly person?"***

Below is what our SuperWellness community shares. See if this resonates for you.

A healthy person tends to:

- bounce back from illness/injury faster than a sickly person
- be confident in his/her capacity to recover from life's stressors
- be open and curious so that he/she can learn from each experience
- be self-aware and skilled at listening to his/her body
- honor the body's process of healing and repair, and give the necessary support (including rest, nutrition, hydration, therapies, etc.) so that it can heal faster
- have access to healing tools or resources to support his/her own health
- embrace all the experiences of life as opportunities to learn and grow
- not be afraid to ask for help, while also being self-directed and self-empowered.

If these attributes distinguish a Healthy person from a less Healthy person, and we all want to be Healthy, then shouldn't we focus on cultivating these attributes?

Rather than running away from illness or injury, we can choose to take this new approach which maximizes our learning and growth from each experience of life.

Once we start looking, we discover that every challenge has its gifts and opportunities. For example, after healing from a bone fracture, that bone will be even stronger than ever before. When we catch a cold or flu, after we recover, our body benefits from lifetime immunity. Once we understand this truth, we begin to see these examples everywhere.

THE DANCE OF YIN AND YANG

In every area of life, we can become fitter, stronger, and more adaptive as a result of balanced cycles of Stress and Recovery. This is a fundamental teaching of Chinese Medicine - the balance of Yin and Yang.

The concept of Yin-Yang balance is simple. When there's too much Yang (activity) and not enough Yin (rest and recovery), we can become overworked, sick, or injured. Conversely, if there is too much Yin (e.g. couch potato) and not enough Yang, we can become sluggish and sick.

Optimal health requires ongoing balanced doses of Yin and Yang.

But Yin and Yang is never a fixed or static state. It's an ever-evolving dynamic dance, because life is not static.

Athletes know this principle of Yin and Yang well. One must train and stress his/her body to grow fitter and stronger (Yang). But it is only during the recovery that the athlete adapts to the training (Yin). The recovery allows him/her to grow fitter, faster, and stronger. He/she must listen to the body to find this balance. Without sufficient recovery, the body cannot adapt and integrate the training, and injuries happen.

No stress, no growth. No recovery, also no growth. Optimal health and performance comes from balanced doses of Yin and Yang.

Here's the fine-print about living a "balanced" life that's rarely mentioned. From time to time, we might take a risk and push ourselves temporarily out of balance, out of our "comfort zone," in order to find a whole new balance!

Sometimes we choose to push ourselves consciously. Sometimes life throws us a curveball and pushes us in unforeseen ways. If we're open to stretching beyond our "comfort zone" and learning and growing from each experience of life, we can tap into grander possibilities. We can become fitter, stronger, and wiser as a result of stretching ourselves.

In the example of the athlete striving for high performance, he/she must be willing to experiment and push the fine line of Yin-Yang balance from time to time. Injuries or illness teach us to fine tune and adjust our programs. The most highly experienced athletes learn from all their past injuries. They know the art of listening deeply to the body, so they can make elegant micro-adjustments at the earliest sign of imbalance, without waiting until a full injury before they course correct.

For all of us, it is this attitude of mindfulness, curiosity, learning, and self-awareness that sets the stage for long-term optimal health. When we understand the ever evolving dance of Yin-Yang balance, we can relax and work with it. We can learn to live in harmony with it and find our higher levels of health, joy, and fulfillment.

I love this quote from Eckhart Tolle which encapsulates the essence of embracing life's ups and downs and learning from each experience:

"Is suffering really necessary? Yes and no. If you had not suffered as you have, there would be no depth to you as a human being. No humility, no compassion. You would not be reading this now. Suffering cracks open the shell of the ego and then comes a point when it has served its purpose. Suffering is necessary until you realize it is unnecessary." ~Eckhart Tolle

So while we would not actively choose to get sick or injured, every illness or injury can be an opportunity for us to become more strong, more wise, more compassionate, more aware, more resilient and more adaptive.

SUPERWELLNESS LAB - YOUR DEFINITION OF HEALTH

Now let's hear your thoughts on this important topic. After contemplating that juicy discussion, **what is your definition of Health?**

Please write out **your** personal definition of health in your journal, and on a piece of paper that you can hang on your wall.

Health is..._____.

Here are some examples of what past SuperWellness participants have shared:

- *"Health is a state of balance and integration of body, mind, emotions, and soul, where we can adapt to life's stressors and grow fitter, stronger, smarter, and wiser with each and every experience."*
- *"Health is the freedom to live my life to the fullest."*
- *"Health is living life in the state of gratitude and unconditional love."*
- *"Health is the confidence in my capacity to recover from all of life's challenges, to evolve into the best version of myself."*
- *"Health is the state of openness and limitless possibilities."*
- *"Health is oneness and connection - first a connection within oneself, and then cultivating a connection with the outer world."*

Such beautiful words of wisdom!

For more inspiration, I invite you to go to:

www.SuperWellness.com/BookBonuses/ Enjoy a rich conversation on this topic with other SuperWellness heroes.

NON-FOOD WAYS OF NOURISHING OUR BODY, MIND, EMOTIONS, AND SOUL

Previously in Chapter 1, we explored why "Eat Right and Exercise" is not the #1 key to our health. While undoubtedly Food and Exercise do play a significant role in our health, we can now appreciate why it's not the be-all-and-end-all that our media has trained us to believe. There are so many lifestyle factors that could be as important, or even more important, than "Eat Right and Exercise!"

Now that we know Health is about balance, integration, openness, connection, personal evolution, and adaptability, what are the best ways to cultivate these?

In Chapter 1's inquiry exercise, you jotted down your favorite **non-food ways** to nourish the body, mind, emotions, and spirit. Now let's continue this theme of "coming Home" as we tap into more of your inner wisdom. I invite you to look back at your answers to Chapter 1 and see if they've evolved.

- What are your favorite non-food ways in which you can **nourish your body**?
- What are your favorite non-food ways to **nourish your mind?**
- What are your favorite non-food ways to **nourish your emotions?**
- What are your favorite non-food ways to **nourish your soul or spirit?**

Please jot down three to five items for each list.

Have you noticed that many of your items are repeating themselves? Please circle the ones that repeat the most.

Common answers from our SuperWellness participants include: *Laughter, Nature and Outdoors, Sunshine, Sleep, Volunteer Service, Massage, Yoga, Music, Singing, Dancing, Quality Time with Friends & Family, Playing with Children, Community, Uplifting Books/Movies/Media, Water, Carving Out Quiet Time to "Do Nothing," Fun Games, Hugs, Snuggle with Kittens/Puppies/Grandchildren... etc.*

Over 15 years working with thousands of patients, I've come to understand that these "non-food" nourishments are the true "Essential Nutrients" for a human being to thrive!

SUPERWELLNESS LAB - YOUR FAVORITE NON-FOOD NOURISHMENTS

Which non-food nourishments are highest priority for you?

Your mission this week: Put the top one, two, or three back into practice and see how it feels.

At this moment, you might be thinking:

"Dr. Edith, this all sounds wonderful, but a little fluffy. How about some scientific evidence that these non-food things are actually beneficial?"

You got it!

When it comes to "Non-Food Nourishment" that benefit our well-being on many levels, my top two favorite tools are:

1. **Breathing**
2. **Gratitude Practice**

If you implement nothing else in this book than these two simple practices, it will already be profoundly life-changing. Here's why.

BREATHING: THE #1 POWER TOOL FOR HEALTH

Conscious Breathing practice is one of the most powerful and fundamental keys to our well-being. Yet it is also the #1 most overlooked.

On our journey of health and healing, most of us have experienced great improvements in our energy and vitality when we clean up our foods and improve our hydration. But how often do we focus on our breathing?

Let's consider this from a pure survival perspective. Food vs. Water vs. Breath.

The medical texts say that a healthy human could theoretically survive for weeks without food, as long as he/she is given water. They also say that an average person could survive without water for a few days (but of course please **do not** test this limit at home without careful medical supervision!). On the other hand, when it comes to breathing, unless you're a highly trained world-class free diver, most people could not survive without breathing for more than a few minutes.

When we look at Breathing, Hydration, and Eating from this fundamental perspective, is it any wonder that healthy Breathing can have the most enormous influence? The best part about it - it's <u>Free</u>!

We tend to take Breathing for granted because it happens automatically without requiring our conscious thought. So unless we have asthma, coughing, wheezing, or lung disease, most of us rarely think about our breathing. But Qigong Masters, Yogis, Alchemists, and Healers across millennia have all focused on the power of Breath as the # 1 tool for conscious self-care and self-healing, and it's for good reason.

- Did you know that the average adult uses only 10-15% of his lung capacity most of the day?[14] Imagine how much more energy we could all feel if we tap into a greater percentage?

- Did you know, even while exercising at "full exertion", most modern adults only access 70% of their lung capacity?[15] But with practice and training, we can leverage closer to 100%. *(Dr. E notes: is it also possible that science doesn't yet know what 100% is?)*

- Did you know, when it comes to removal of waste products, the vast majority, i.e. **70%**, is expelled through the breath? Only a small percentage is removed through sweat, urine, and bowels?[16] We all know how toxic and inflamed we can feel when we're constipated and bowels aren't moving. But breathing is even more critical for healthy detox and cleansing than the bowels!

Surely we've all had direct personal experience with the calming and soothing effects of taking just a few deep breaths.

Below are 20 known benefits of breathing:
- Breathing helps to calm our mind;
- Breathing increases energy and clarity;
- Breathing can elevate mood;
- Breathing removes waste and toxins from the body;
- Breathing can reduce physical, mental, and emotional tension;
- Breathing helps us to burn fat more effectively;
- Breathing helps us optimize our body weight;
- Breathing massages our internal organs;
- Breathing helps to reduce pain;
- Breathing assists with healthy posture from inside out;

- Breathing can improve sleep;
- Breathing can reduce trauma symptoms;
- Breathing helps us regulate our emotions;
- Breathing can improve addiction/impulsivity;
- Breathing can deepen our meditative experience in profound ways;
- Breathing improves our intuitive abilities;
- Breathing enhances creativity;
- Breathing improves cellular regeneration;
- Breathing allows us to influence our Autonomic Nervous System;
- Breathing can enhance our mojo and serve as a natural aphrodisiac;
- Best of all, Breathing is FREE! [17] [18]

There are many powerful systems of conscious breathing practice out there. If you already have a favorite breathwork practice, I encourage you to bring it back into your daily self-care routine.

One of my favorite systems is the Wim Hof Method, which includes conscious breathing practice, cold acclimatization, and mind training. It's my favorite because of its simplicity, and because it's the very first one to be studied so rigorously by science.

There are a number of studies now confirming the benefits and mechanism of action of the Wim Hof Method. A particularly groundbreaking study was published in 2014 in the *Proceedings of the National Academy of Science.*

In this study, scientists injected a bacteria endotoxin into Wim Hof and 24 healthy volunteers. Normally, this endotoxin causes strong flu-like symptoms (chills, fever, bodyache, headaches, nausea, vomiting, etc.), until the healthy body clears it after some hours with the uncomfortable symptoms. For this study, half the volunteers were trained by Wim on his techniques for only a few days. The other half served as the control group and received no training. (The poor control-group guys!)

The results changed the medical textbooks forever.

While the control group suffered all the uncomfortable flu-like symptoms as expected, all members of the trained group were able to influence their autonomic nervous system and immune system to clear the toxins without the uncomfortable flu-like symptoms! 100% of them![19]

In other words, the so-called Autonomic Nervous System is not actually "autonomous." It can be consciously influenced.

The authors concluded that this finding *"could have important implications for the treatment of conditions associated with excessive or persistent inflammation, such as autoimmune disease."*

There's a phenomenal VICE documentary on Wim Hof called *"Inside the Superhuman World of the Iceman."* It will open you to exciting and awesome new possibilities.

The implications of these studies are truly astounding. We can all go deeply within ourselves and influence our Autonomic Nervous System, Immune System, and Endocrine System far deeper than ever thought possible.

Wim loves to say *"Feeling is understanding."* The depth of this kind of inner-power is hard to believe until we experience it directly and see for ourselves. So beginning today, I invite you to take back your power and Breathe.

SUPERWELLNESS LAB - BREATHING & QIGONG ENERGIZER

On a scale of 1 - 10, where is your Energy level right now?

In your Chapter 3 Book Bonuses, you'll find a simple Breathing and Qigong exercise. Go there now to learn the exact same quick energizer routine I showed the Reddit employees that took their energy from a 3 to a 10. I like to kickstart each and every day with this routine. Be amazed at how quickly you can shift your energy state, on demand.

Enjoy your Breathing & Qigong Energizer video now at:

www.SuperWellness.com/BookBonuses/

How was your Breathing and Qigong exercise? How do you feel now? Scale of 1 - 10, are you back at 8, 9, or 10?

Imagine how much money you could save, if you don't need that Starbucks to get the morning going? Or that mid-afternoon latte to combat the lull in your energy? Let's say you spend $5/day on your Venti latte. That could add up to $1500 a year! What beautiful things would you do with that extra money instead?

Your mission this week:

- Simple mindfulness - take a moment at the beginning and end of each day to check-in with your Energy level.
- Enjoy the Breathing and Qigong Energizer practice **at least once a day** every day for this upcoming week. Put it on your calendar to practice daily, and be blown away by the result.

Success tip: Make it easy, make it fun! Practice just 10 minutes a day this week, and allow the results to surprise you!

GRATITUDE PRACTICE: THE OTHER #1 POWER TOOL!

Let's do another simple exercise.

On a scale of 1 - 10, how would you rate your level of **joy** and **contentment** right now?

Now, think of the most beautiful experience you had in the past week. Can you go back into that sweet memory and relive it? Think of three things about it for which you feel most grateful. Three things that warm your heart and make you smile.

Close your eyes. Really see, sense, feel into each of these three things.

As you review your Gratitudes, how is your level of joy and contentment? Did it shift?

Our minds are so incredible. We all know from direct experience that the state of Gratitude is powerful medicine. It's a much-needed antidote to the enormous stresses of our world today, don't you agree? It's no wonder that every personal growth expert - from Tony Robbins to Eckhart Tolle to Oprah Winfrey - all emphasize Gratitude as the secret sauce to long-term health, joy, happiness, and success.

For inspiration, below are some of my favorite quotes on this topic of gratitude.

"Gratitude turns what we have into enough, and more. It turns denial into acceptance, chaos into order, confusion into clarity...it makes sense of our past, brings peace for today, and creates a vision for tomorrow."

~Melody Beattie

"It is impossible to feel grateful and depressed in the same moment." ~Naomi Williams

"Gratitude also opens your eyes to the limitless potential of the universe, while dissatisfaction closes your eyes to it." ~Stephen Richards

"This is a wonderful day. I've never seen this one before."

~Maya Angelou

"Things turn out best for people who make the best of the way things turn out." ~John Wooden

"Enjoy the little things, for one day you may look back and realize they were the big things." ~Robert Brault

"Gratitude is the healthiest of all human emotions. The more you express gratitude for what you have, the more likely you will have even more to express gratitude for."

~Zig Ziglar

"Gratitude is the currency that we can mint for ourselves and spend without fear of bankruptcy."

~Fred De Witt Van Amburgh

"When you are grateful, fear disappears and abundance appears." ~Tony Robbins

"Be thankful for what you have; you'll end up having more. If you concentrate on what you don't have, you will never, ever have enough." ~Oprah Winfrey

"If you want to turn your life around, try thankfulness. It will change your life mightily." ~Gerald Good

"Acknowledging the good that you already have in your life is the foundation for all abundance." ~*Eckhart Tolle*

There is no denying that Gratitude can enhance our experience of life. But for most of us, this state of Gratitude comes and goes sporadically, as if by chance.

So how do we cultivate the attitude of Gratitude more consistently?

How can we make Gratitude our default state?

By now, I'm sure you've heard about the practice of "**Gratitude Journaling**", the practice of simply writing three or five things in a journal each day, things for which you feel grateful.

"Oh, Dr. Edith. That sounds so hokey - does it really work?"

Here's what the research says. People who use a Gratitude Journal experience:

- better energy
- increased alertness and attentiveness
- better quality of sleep
- enhanced immunity
- increased productivity
- less stress or anxiety
- less missed days of work
- healthier blood pressure levels
- improved creativity, communication, and collaboration in the workplace
- higher success in achieving goals
- improved long-term happiness and life-satisfaction.[20] [21]

Gratitude practice is truly the secret sauce to long-term health, joy, and happiness.

"Woah! Are you serious? All of this by jotting three simple things down in a journal once a day? I'm in!"

SUPERWELLNESS LAB - GRATITUDE PRACTICE

If you'd like to dive deeper into the Science of Gratitude, please enjoy the video in your Chapter 3 book bonuses:

(www.SuperWellness.com/BookBonuses/)

Research suggests that it can take 21 days to shift our habits into a new default state. This has been my experience with clients as well. While there's instant gratification every time we write down our Gratitudes, it is by committing to a full 21-day practice that we experience longer-term results.

So please join me and our global community of SuperWellness heroes. Let's commit to a 21-Day Gratitude Journal practice starting today. For the next 21 days, jot down three things each day that you feel grateful for.

As you experience the Gratitude practice, take note of your energy, productivity, sleep, mental focus, etc.. Find out for yourself how Gratitude practice can enhance your life!

SUMMARY OF 'H' IS FOR HOME

In this chapter, we journeyed Home to ourselves, returning to our inner wisdom. We discovered why some of the most potent and empowering tools are already available to all of us, right here, right now. This is very good news indeed!

We explored:

- The simplicity of Mindfulness
- <u>Your</u> definition of Health
- How a healthy person responds to illness/injury vs. a less healthy person

- The dynamic dance of Yin and Yang balance
- Implementing your favorite non-food ways of nourishing yourself
- Why Breathing practice may be the #1 most powerful tool for health
- Why Gratitude is the secret sauce to a healthy, joyful, and fulfilling life.

For your **SuperWellness Lab** this week, please:

1. Share your new definition of Health with our community.
2. Put into practice 1-3 non-food lifestyle habits that nourish you.
3. Enjoy the Daily Breathing (and Qigong) Energizer practice – 10 minutes 1x/day.
4. Begin a Gratitude Journal - jotting down 3 things each day for which you feel grateful.

Have FUN with it!

I feel confident that, if you implement the principles of this chapter alone, your life will be enhanced in profound ways. The key is putting these simple ideas into **consistent** practice.

To support your SuperWellness journey, be sure to claim your book bonuses at www.SuperWellness.com/BookBonus/ Log-on to the SuperWellness community forum for friendship and support. We're all waiting to hear from you!

In the next chapter, we're going to take the idea of non-food nourishments to a whole other level, by exploring how our Environment feeds and nurtures our health. **"E" is for Environment.** I'm going to share with you how changing only my Environment (without any change in Diet or Exercise), completely altered my sleep, energy, fertility cycles, and more.

Let's discover how to create an ideal Environment to feel Energized and Electrified!

CHAPTER 4
'E' is for Environment

"Nature's peace will flow into you as sunshine flows into trees. The winds will blow their own freshness into you, and the storms their energy, while cares will drop away from you like the leaves of Autumn."

~ *John Muir* ~

NATURE AND YOUR MOJO

Question for you: Have you ever had the experience where you felt stuck in a rut, unsure what to do next? Then the answer comes to you in a *flash of insight* after a nourishing day out in Nature?

Maybe it was after a scenic hike? Maybe it was a beautiful sunset? Maybe you felt inspired and reinvigorated after a day at the beach or a great night's sleep?

At our clinic in San Francisco, many patients tell us they feel stressed out, overwhelmed, and restless for change. We're all hungry for more peace, more joy, more clarity. While each person comes into the clinic for a different "chief complaint" (such as back pain, headache, digestion, etc.), there's a common theme of chronic stress at the root of nearly every case these days.

"Dr. E, can you make all this stress and overwhelm go away? I just want to find my mojo and zest for life again!"

Have you been there too?

Our community is filled with amazing people - entrepreneurs, supermoms, superdads, successful professionals, community builders, and visionary leaders. But on the journey of achievement and success, many of us find ourselves sacrificing our quality of life and often, our health. The more successful we are, the more others will demand of us.

Our modern technology offers many great efficiencies and conveniences, but we're also being inundated with constant noise, distraction and overwhelm, and it's taking its toll on our health.

How can we create a better balance? An environment that gives us less stress, less overwhelm, more energy, more clarity and inspiration?

The fact is, most of us sit indoors all day at the computer. We breathe stale recycled air and work under unhealthy artificial lighting. We rarely see sunlight during the day, and we don't receive true restful darkness at night. **Our energy and circadian rhythms have become badly out-of-sync with nature's cycles.**

Many of us don't sleep well at night, and we don't have good energy during the day. Meanwhile we're given more technology in an attempt to solve our problems - this app to learn mindfulness, another app to track our diet, and yet another app to track our exercise.

I love my apps too. But from time to time, we must ask: *"Is all this tech truly simplifying and enhancing our lives? Or inundating us with never-ending noise and distractions?"*

Over my last 15 years working with thousands of clients, I've been blown away by how the most **simple shifts in our Environment can yield the most potent results**.

Environment factors like

- natural Sunlight during the day,
- restful Darkness at night,
- taking breaks from electronic screen-time,

- more physical contact with Nature, and
- daily conscious breathing practice.

As we optimize our Environment and restore natural circadian rhythms, our physiology responds rapidly! The results are often mind-blowing.

Within days, hours, even minutes of implementing these shifts, we can feel **more vibrant, clear, and energized**. We return to our natural state of balance and well-being.

In this state, we feel well-rested at night and energized during the day. Fun, creativity and inspiration flow naturally. The answers to life's greatest challenges often come in surprisingly joyful and effortless ways. Instead of struggling and "toughing it out", solutions arise when we're well-rested, relaxed and playful.

Optimizing our Environment is KEY to better Energy. Not only does it enhance our health and well-being, it can shift our entire perspective on life.

In 2013, I experienced this lesson directly when I recalibrated my "Environment" in a massive way.

DISCOVERING THE GIFT OF LIGHT & DARKNESS

Have you ever heard of a meditation practice called "Dark Room Retreat?"

As the name suggests, you meditate in a completely dark space for days or weeks continuously. It's an unusual retreat designed for long-term meditation practitioners who feel called to deepen their practice. But fair warning: it's not for everybody.

In March 2013, I travelled to Thailand for an **"11-Day Dark Room Retreat"** led by a world-renowned meditation teacher named **Jasmuheen**.

Dark room is considered a sacred (some say, highly-guarded) practice used in many traditions across the world - the ancient Yogis, the Qigong Masters, the Egyptian Alchemists, the Indigenous Kogi Mamas of Columbia, to name a few. The darkness allows practitioners to drop into unusually deep states of stillness and gain greater access to visionary insights and inner wisdom.

For me, it delivered all that and much much more. In those 11 days, I received more gifts and learned more about life than in my previous decade of meditation combined.

Every question that I brought into the retreat was answered. I walked out of the retreat rejuvenated, refreshed and inspired, with a new understanding of life itself. So many powerful gifts, I look forward to writing a future book to share with you!

Of the 11 days, we spent **nine days and nine nights meditating in complete darkness.** The first and last days are for acclimatization and integration. The core nine days and nights are spent in a state of continuous meditation, with periodic guided practices led by Jasmuheen.

The retreat was held at the beautiful Tao Garden outside Chiang Mai, in the Southeastern foothills of the Himalayas. Tao Garden was founded by the renowned Taoist Qigong master Mantak Chia. He meticulously architected this building for the practice of Dark Room Meditation, using special earthen materials to mimic the energetic experience of a Yogi meditating in a dark cave.

The building was uniquely designed so that not a single photon of light could enter from the outside. Staff members wore night-vision goggles to clean and service the building and deliver juices and water. To prevent us from bumping into corners, there's thick padding covering every turn or pillar in the building. The space was well equipped with all the modern amenities (like private bedrooms, fresh linens, bathroom, shower, healthy airflow, etc.) and none of the dangers that ancient Yogis had to contend with in a dark cave, such as snakes or scorpions!

Several times a day, Jasmuheen led beautiful guided meditations, cocooning our space in the most loving and healing energies. She was available around the clock for added support. On the one hand, dark room meditation can be a very intense initiation. On the other hand, this was the most supportive 5-star experience. A gift of cosmic proportions!

Talk about a "change in environment!" We were completely unhooked from the outside world. There were no phones or computers, no TV, no internet, no reading of books, no distractions at all. Just complete stillness and darkness for nine days and nights.

Not one single photon of light could enter the building.

Rather than feeling anxious or uneasy in the darkness, I was pleasantly surprised to find the darkness to be profoundly nourishing! Living in bright cities all my life (Hong Kong, then Boston, Cambridge, Washington D.C., and now San Francisco), I had never experienced true darkness like this before. It occurred to me that **most of us spend our lives under artificial lighting and have never experienced complete darkness at night.**

It felt so nourishing that I realized I had been "hungry" for this darkness all my life.

Imagine if you'd been living in polluted cities all your life, half holding your breath. Then for the first time ever, you go to a pristine forest filled with lush redwood trees and pure oxygen-rich air. Can you imagine what that **first** deep breath of fresh air feels like? For me, the experience of Darkness was like that. So delicious. So rejuvenating.

Sometimes we don't know what we're missing, until we do.

For the first three days in darkness, I slept like a baby for what seemed like 14 to 16 hours each day. I had no idea I was so sleep deprived! Then after the third day, I felt so well-rested that there was no more "hunger" for sleep. Even though we were free to wake or sleep whenever we liked, I found myself staying awake 24 x 7 in the darkness, in an ever deepening state of blissful meditation. Visionary insights and inspiration flooded in continuously in the state of peace, clarity, and tranquility.

"Sleep deprivation" is normally torturously painful. But here in the darkness, I felt the exact opposite - totally relaxed, peaceful, and inspired. I was doing yoga in my room and receiving rapid flows of meditative insights around the clock. No sleep, but so profoundly relaxed and well-rested.

Could it be that when we say that we need sleep, we're largely hungry for rejuvenating darkness and a peaceful mind?

Interestingly, I felt so nourished by the deep rest in darkness, that all my physical hunger went away. As you likely know, fasting can have many health benefits if done with thoughtfulness and care. (Caution: I do not recommend anyone stop eating or do prolonged fasts without careful medical supervision.) However, in this dark retreat, I never felt any hunger and fasted effortlessly and naturally. In fact, it felt more like a feast![1]

Science tells us that sleep deprivation can decrease Leptin levels (the satiety hormone). This makes us feel more hungry and unsatiated, slowing our metabolism and increasing the risk of obesity and related conditions. When we're sleep deprived, we might eat until the stomach is full and still feel hungry. Have you had that experience? Pulling a stressful "all-nighter" and craving sugar, fat, and high-calorie foods the next morning? Here in the dark retreat, it seemed that the opposite was happening. Perhaps I "saturated my sleep needs" which left me feeling totally satiated?

There were so many fascinating and surprising experiences. I look forward to sharing with you in the future.

Finally, on the last day of the retreat, our big moment arrived! Coming out of the dark into the light again. We emerged from the Dark Room at sunset, wearing sunglasses to gently transition back to the world of physical vision and light. As I took the sunglasses off... I was speechless.

The intense beauty. The multi-dimensional colors and lights.

Seeing our world for the very first time.

It took my breath away.

The sunset, the flowers, the trees, the earth, and the entire scene with all its exquisite details - there was a new depth and new dimensionality that I had never seen before. I marveled for hours, stunned by the awe-inspiring beauty that had always been there, but I never had the eyes to perceive it until now.

The next morning, watching the magnificent Sunrise brought unexpected tears and waves of gratitude again.

I realized that our world is far from mundane. It has always been so stunningly beautiful. I was simply un-attuned before.

---

[1] *As soon as the retreat was complete, I went to the on-site medical clinic for thorough blood tests, to examine the physiological effects of my retreat. With the exception of Vitamin D being low (as expected), all other blood markers showed perfect optimum health!*

Gradually the intensity of the colors softened as my eyes adjusted. But the experience enriched my life forever. I fell in love with Nature's exquisite beauty and gained a brand new appreciation for the dance of Light and Darkness.

Today, I've come to see that our Environment can alter our perception of life in profound ways. **Light, Darkness, and Nature are "Essential Nutrients" for our health and well-being**. As a human being and as a holistic doctor, I've come to see these as even more important than "diet and exercise."

The great news is, we don't need to go away to Thailand to enjoy these benefits! They are available to each of us for free, wherever we are, through **simple shifts** that we can put into practice right away.

I invite you to experiment with your Environment this week and see for yourself.

SUPERWELLNESS LAB - A SELF-ASSESSMENT OF YOUR ENVIRONMENT

How do you feel your Environment is influencing your well-being?

Let's take inventory of your typical daily interactions with your Environment. These factors play a key role in your energy, vitality, and metabolism, as well as your mental, emotional and physical well-being.

- How much of your day is spent indoors under artificial lighting?
- Do you take breaks to go outside and receive natural sunlight during your day?
- How many hours each day do you spend in front of a digital screen?
- How much time per week do you spend outdoors in nature? Have you ever hugged a tree? Is it possible those hippies are onto something? (smiles)

- When was the last time you went barefoot on the grass, or at the beach, making physical contact with the earth to receive the earth's abundant flow of electrons to balance your energy and electricity?
- When was the last time you watched a beautiful sunrise or sunset?
- How would you rate your quality of sleep?
- Do you sleep in a peaceful environment and in complete darkness?

How did you do? In this chapter we will dive deep into each of these areas. So please keep your answers in mind as you read on.

Let us explore the science and practical tools for optimizing the three key aspects of Environment:

1) **Sleeping in complete Darkness at night,**
2) **Exposure to natural Sunlight during the day,**
3) **Physical contact with Nature.**

SLEEPING IN COMPLETE DARKNESS AT NIGHT

Tell me. How's your sleep?

Do you have a completely dark environment for your sleep? Are you sleeping enough? From what time to what time? Is it good quality? Do you bounce out of bed in the morning, feeling recharged and ready to take on your day?

Insomnia is one of the most common complaints that bring patients to our clinic.

Research shows that roughly 30 to 50% of us have insomnia from time to time, and 10% suffer from chronic insomnia.[22] If you have insomnia, I recommend visiting your health practitioner for professional support, in addition to exploring the lifestyle changes in this section.

Even amongst patients who do not have Insomnia, many of us are suffering from some amount of "Chronic Partial Sleep Deprivation," i.e. not enough sleep. We live in a society that pushes us to go-go-go. Our exposure to technology and artificial lighting keeps our circadian rhythms chronically out-of-sync with nature. We all know from direct experience how good it feels after a great night's sleep - the clarity, the vitality, and the access to insights. But we aren't necessarily aware how detrimental sleep deprivation can be.

Research tells us that when we're chronically sleep deprived, we tend to misjudge our own levels of exhaustion. We aren't always self-aware of the cognitive and physical impairments. Sometimes we need objective scientific research to remind us what we already feel intuitively.

The scientific journals are flooded with fascinating research on the benefits and importance of sleep.

Here's my top 12 list of scientifically-proven benefits of Sleep:

- Sleep lowers stress levels;
- Sleep decreases depression or anxiety;
- Sleep sharpens attention;
- Sleep improves memory and learning;
- Sleep helps us to avoid accidents;
- Sleep decreases inflammation (lowering your rate of heart disease, stroke, diabetes, arthritis, aging);
- Sleep enhances immune function (decreasing colds, flus, cancers, and more);
- Sleep can spur creativity;
- Sleep enhances athletic performance;
- Sleep helps to optimizes body weight;
- Sleep can increase satiation and decrease food cravings;
- Sleep promotes beauty, youthfulness and longevity; [23] [24]

You may have heard that the "sleep hormone" melatonin is only produced by the pineal gland in an environment of darkness. But did you know that melatonin is much more than a "sleep hormone?" It's more accurate to call it the "darkness hormone" because melatonin is produced in darkness and offers an enormous range of benefits far beyond sleep.

Melatonin has been found to be:
- immune-boosting,
- anti-inflammatory,
- anti-cancer,
- neuroprotective,
- preventive of cardiovascular events & type 2 diabetes, and
- relieving of heartburn or GERD symptoms,

    just to name a few! [25] [26] [27]

Did you know? Research shows that night shift workers, despite sleeping "enough hours" can have increased rates of many chronic diseases, including certain cancers, metabolic problems, heart disease, ulcers, gastrointestinal problems, diabetes, and obesity.[28] For these reasons, I always encourage my patients who are night shift workers to make it their #1 priority to change to the day shift as soon as possible.

Meanwhile, even though most of us are not nightshift workers, many aspects of life still tempt us into a chronically sleep deprived routine that's out-of-sync with nature's cycles. The science is clear about the health consequences of sleep deprivation or night-time melatonin deficiency, as well as the far-reaching benefits of quality sleep and darkness. Perhaps it's time to re-prioritize our sleep hygiene again.

My Darkroom experience taught me that sometimes we don't know what we're missing, until we try something new. If you want better vitality and energy to create a truly extraordinary life, I encourage you to sleep your way to the top!

SUPERWELLNESS RECIPE FOR GETTING THE BEST NIGHT'S SLEEP

- **#1 priority:** Make sure you see natural sunlight in the morning and daytime, and contrast it with complete darkness at night. This helps your brain (and body) to re-synchronize with nature's circadian rhythm.

- Minimize bright screen-time in the evening (TV, computer, iPad, phone, etc.) especially within two hours of bedtime.

- If you must use electronic devices in the evening, make sure to install a blue-light blocking app on your devices (like f.lux), so that the screen transitions into the softer, more relaxing orange hue. Over-exposure to the blue-light, especially in the evening, can disrupt our circadian rhythms and night-time melatonin production.

- You can also wear blue-light blocking glasses (they look orange and are easily found online).

- Many of my patients have noticed that Wifi and EMF fields seem to influence their sleep. As an experiment, try turning off your Wifi hub at night and put your devices on airplane-mode or turn them off. (e.g. you can connect your Wifi hub to a timer plug that automatically shuts it off from 10pm-6am.) Move all EMF-generating electronics farther from your bedroom where possible.

- Research studies have consistently found that most of us do best with eight hours of sleep, with the most restorative sleep within the hours of **11pm to 3am**.[29] Of course, lifestyle factors are never one-size-fits-all. So please test it out for yourself. Try sleeping eight hours every night this week, and be sure to include the magic 11pm to 3am window, and see how you feel! Experiment and decide for yourself.

- Cultivate a consistent relaxing bedtime routine. E.g. take a warm bath, write in your gratitude journal, listen to relaxing bedtime music, try essential oil aromatherapy, or put on your favorite jammies!

- **Most importantly, create a completely Dark environment for your sleep.** E.g. draw the thick curtains or blinds, turn off all light-emitting devices, remove any night lights or even tiny LED lights within visible range from your bed, and/or sleep with an eye mask on.

Many of my patients who have insomnia or sleeplessness are relieved to learn that the benefits of Melatonin come from exposure to Darkness at night. Please remember that Melatonin is the "Darkness Hormone." Whether or not you're asleep, just continue to rest, breathe and relax in the darkness. Perhaps you enjoy some relaxing music or guided meditations. The most detrimental thing you could do is turn on bright lights, or stare at your smartphones or computers! The restorative, immune-boosting, and neuroprotective effects of melatonin come only from the darkness.

So sleep or no sleep, I invite you to give yourself the gift of complete darkness, seven to eight hours each night, including the 11pm to 3am window. You may be amazed how rested you feel even if you're not fully asleep.

If you suffer from chronic insomnia, please seek support from a professional healthcare practitioner. Restoring quality sleep is one of the best investments in your long-term health. You deserve to live long and healthy!

For more supportive resources on sleep, be sure to check out your book bonuses for this chapter and share your comments and questions on our community forum. www.SuperWellness.com/BookBonuses/

―――――――――

NATURAL SUNLIGHT DURING THE DAY

By now, I'm sure you've heard that Vitamin D, "the Sunshine Vitamin," is critical for human health and well-being. We know that Vitamin D is important for

- building strong bones,
- regulating calcium in our body,
- supporting mood, brain, and nerve function,

- optimizing immune function (decreasing our chances of colds, flus, allergies, some cancers and autoimmune diseases),
- boosting weight loss in those who are overweight,
- preventing depression,
- and more! [30]

That's why I recommend all of my patients test their Vitamin D levels regularly. Because of our modern indoor lifestyles, the vast majority of my patients are quite deficient in Vitamin D when we first meet them. After Vitamin D levels are optimized, we see massive improvement in all aspects of their health (energy, mood, immune function and more!). So I encourage you to talk with your healthcare provider about monitoring and optimizing your Vitamin D level as part of your ongoing preventative care.

While we can take a Vitamin D supplement to optimize Vitamin D levels, it's important to remember that **full spectrum Sunlight offers many benefits far beyond just Vitamin D production.**

"But Dr. E, I thought I should avoid the sun at all costs, so I don't get skin damage or skin cancer?"

Yes, I've heard that one too. But not only does that go against most of our personal experience (don't you sometimes just crave the sun?), it's not what the research says.

A March 2016 study published in the Journal of Internal Medicine found that **Sun avoidance may have a strong negative influence to our life expectancy at a magnitude similar to smoking**!

The researchers followed 30,000 women over the span of 20 years and discovered that, **compared to Sun-avoiders, Sunbathers were found to have** *"lower risk of Cardiovascular disease, and other diseases such as diabetes, multiple sclerosis, and pulmonary disease."* [31] [32]

Of course we don't want to damage our skin with sunburns, but could it be that Sunshine, like most things in life, has an optimal range? Not too much, and not too little. Just the right dose.

It turns out the scientific evidence supporting moderate doses of sun has been published for decades. A 1993 study titled *"Beneficial Effects of Sun Exposure on Mortality"* found that regular sun exposure decreased rates of death across all types of cancers. Specifically with regards to Melanoma, they found that severe burns increased the risk, but regular non-burning exposure to sunshine decreased the risk.[33]

A recent 2016 meta-analysis study called *"The Risks and Benefits of Sun Exposure 2016"* confirms this finding. After reviewing all the best available literature, the authors concluded that regular exposure to **non-burning sun** offered an enormous range of health benefits, including decreased cancer, cardiovascular disease, Alzheimer disease/dementia, myopia and macular degeneration, diabetes and multiple sclerosis, to name a few.[34]

It's also interesting to note that ancient traditional cultures all around the world - e.g. the Yogis, the Qigong masters, the Mayans, the Egyptians - have valued sun-salutations, sun-gazing, or sun-worshiping practices throughout millennia.

Is it time for us to bring back a more sensible and balanced relationship with the sun?

Here are some important keys to consider:

- Exposure to natural Sunlight has been found to enhance the production of Serotonin, which elevates our mood.
- Full-spectrum light therapy (via Sunlight or full-spectrum light bulb) can be a helpful treatment for S.A.D. (seasonal affective disorder), or the "winter blues." [35]
- The Sun's UV rays, especially UV-B rays, may help heal a variety of skin conditions like Eczema and Psoriasis.[36]
- The UV rays (particularly UV-C rays) have antimicrobial properties to help kill harmful bacteria, viruses, and funguses.[37]
- Light exposure has been shown to increase testosterone and sexual satisfaction in men with low libido![38]
- Adequate natural light during the day, combined with darkness at night, re-synchronizes our circadian rhythm and helps us restore energy during the day, and quality sleep at night.
- Exposure to light has been found to enhance ATP production, which provides more energy to the body, and can enhance the healing rate of injured tissues.[39]

- UV light has been found to lower blood pressure, increase the efficiency of the heart, and improve EKG readings in patients with atherosclerosis (hardening of arteries).[40]

- Did you know? Red light therapy has been found by NASA to protect bones and muscles of astronauts in zero gravity.[41]

- Did you know? Blue light therapy is the standard-of-care treatments in hospitals for jaundiced babies?[42]

- Light therapy was once an accepted part of mainstream medicine until the 1930s. With the invention of Penicillin, our medical system focused much more on profitable pharmaceutical solutions and largely abandoned our studies of inexpensive (or free) methods such as light therapy. Is it possible that we know far too little about the healing properties of light, because of insufficient profits to fund the scientific research?[43]

If this topic of Healing with Light fascinates you as much as it does me, I recommend reading the classic book *"Light: Medicine of the Future"* by Dr. Jacob Liberman.

There are so many interesting facets to how Light interacts with our body that science has yet to fully understand. In the next chapter, we'll also explore the latest scientific discoveries about how Light interacts with Water.

Dr. Gerald Pollack, professor of bioengineering at University of Washington discovered that Water can act like a rechargeable solar battery under the influence of Light! Since our human body is mostly water, what are the implications of this for our health? Does this mean that our body is really a hybrid vehicle that can be partially solar-powered? More on this in the next chapter.

One final note about Light. Did you know that the Hemoglobin in our human red blood cells is nearly identical to the Chlorophyll in plants? The only difference is that Chlorophyll has Magnesium in the center of the molecule, and Hemoglobin has Iron in the center. The rest of the molecule is exactly the same.

We all know that Chlorophyll in plants is responsible for converting light and water into physical nutrition. We're told that Hemoglobin is responsible for carrying oxygen. But is there more to it?

Is it possible that Hemoglobin may share similar properties to Chlorophyll, interacting with Light in ways that science has yet to understand?

All the mystical and spiritual traditions across the world say that we are "Beings of Light." Perhaps one day we'll see that this is not just a metaphor, but a fact of our physiology.

I don't have all the answers, but I invite you to ask these fascinating questions together with me. I believe that, in the very near future, our science will discover more and more of these answers with exciting implications for our health.

"Wow, Dr. Edith, this is seriously next level stuff! But how do I apply this to my lifestyle?"

SUPERWELLNESS RECIPE FOR SUN AND LIGHT

Our circadian rhythm influences all aspects of our health and physiology. Exposure to the right kind of light, and at the right time of day, can benefit our energy, metabolism, circulation, and sleep in profound ways.

Below are recommended strategies to restore your circadian rhythm with natural lighting.

Note: There is no one-size-fits-all recommendation here. *If you've been "living like a vampire" for decades, best to ease back to the sun very gently and gradually. Give yourself the benefits of full-spectrum UV Light during the day. Not too much, not too little. Please find your own healthy balance.*

- **Experience Sunrises and/or Sunsets.** Become re-acquainted with the timing of sunrise and sunset in your area again. Go outside to enjoy the beautiful sunrise and sunset on a daily basis. This practice will help to re-synchronize your brain, and therefore your body, to a more optimal circadian rhythm. This is beneficial even if just for a few moments.

- **Expose your body to non-burning Sun during the day.** Besides sunrise and sunset time, go outside at least one other time in the middle of the day when there is non-burning sunlight. E.g.: Go for a walk mid-day, or enjoy your lunch outside when weather permits. Always use your judgement - don't burn your skin, but don't be a complete "sun avoider" either.

- **Optional: Read about Sungazing and decide for yourself.** Sungazing, or solar gazing, is a somewhat controversial practice of gazing at the sun during sunrise or sunset time. Proponents of Sungazing emphasize the fact that UV Index is zero during the first 45minutes after sunrise and the last 45 minutes before sunset, so these are the safest windows to admire a sunrise or sunset. Because most of us are not acclimated to the sun, Sungazing practitioners usually recommend starting with less than 10 seconds only. As always, do your own research about the safety guidelines and decide for yourself.

- <u>**WARNING:**</u> <u>Prolonged gazing at the sun, even during the sunrise and sunset windows can be injurious to the eyes. Please do your research, be very safe and conservative.</u> If we always listen to our body and use common sense, in my personal experience, admiring the sunrise or sunset can be a highly relaxing, beautiful and therapeutic experience.

A growing body of evidence suggests that too much artificial lighting can confuse our physiology. The limited and/or uneven bandwidth of light frequencies in artificial light (such as LEDs or fluorescents) can impact our energy, hormones, metabolism, and more. If interested, I recommend you do your own research to learn more.

To minimize the negative impact of artificial indoor lighting:

- **Introduce full spectrum light back into your indoor environment.** Please experiment by replacing your fluorescents and LED light bulbs with more <u>full-spectrum incandescent light bulbs.</u>[44] E.g.: if you're in an office with artificial light, you can bring a desk lamp with a full-spectrum light bulb. Our clients and students consistently report feeling a major improvement when they live under more full spectrum natural lighting. Test this for yourself and see how you feel.

- **Install blue-light blocking apps or use blue-light blocking glasses in the evenings.** To decrease your exposure to bright blue light during the evenings, which creates the greatest confusion to your circadian rhythm, please install or activate your blue light blocking app, which now comes standard with many digital devices. Blue-light blocking glasses are also an effective alternative. Studies have found that those exposed to bright light in the very early morning and in the evenings have higher insulin resistance, and therefore higher risk for diabetes.[45]

- **Use a "Sunrise Alarm Clock."** If you have trouble waking up in the morning because your bedroom does not get morning sunlight, try using a Sunrise Alarm Clock. This type of alarm clock simulates a gradual sunrise in your bedroom using a full-spectrum incandescent light bulb. This can help resynchronize your circadian rhythm to wake up more naturally.

There's no one right way. Do your own experiments, have fun, and see how you feel!

"But Dr. Edith, what about **sunscreen?** *If I go outside during the day, shouldn't I always wear sunscreen?"*

If you burn easily, or have concerns about skin cancer, I recommend simply avoiding the sun altogether during the peak hours in the middle of the day when UV index is at its highest and the risk of sunburn is high. You can always stay under the shade and/or cover with long-sleeves and hats. If you do want to use sunscreen, I recommend using mineral based sunscreens (e.g. Zinc Oxide cream) that do not have toxic ingredients like oxybenzone, avobenzone, octisalate, octocrylene, homosalate and octinoxate. These chemicals are known hormone disrupters. Please do your research and choose an organic and non-toxic sunscreen.

The truth is, we can have different reactions to the sun at different times.

For some of us, it may be an issue of gradual acclimatization to the sun vs. an all-or-nothing approach. Many of us live completely indoor lifestyles Monday through Friday, with no exposure to sunlight. Then we "sun binge" in an attempt to make up for all our outdoor activities on the weekends. It's the classic "weekend warriors" syndrome. Could this all-or-nothing approach put us at higher risk of sunburns and skin damage?

As I look back through my own life, I've also noticed that each time I got a sunburn, it was when I was already inflamed on the inside. The sun was just one of the multiple factors at play. For example, if I was sleep deprived, poorly hydrated, up all night eating pizzas and drinking beers, then when I'd go out in the sun, my skin would burn very quickly! On the other hand, when I am on a healing yoga or meditation retreat, sleeping plenty, breathing, no stress, lots of juicing, eating clean, and staying well hydrated, I find myself playing under the sun for prolonged periods without sun burns.

Perhaps you've had these experiences too?

The issue of sun exposure may not be as black-and-white as we've been told. The sun is a powerful force that interacts with us in dynamic ways. I believe we're now outgrowing the old paradigm of "Sun is all bad" or "Sun is all good" into a more balanced and mature relationship with it.

Let us bring a new level of intelligence and wisdom to our lifestyle. Rather than one-size-fits-all prescriptions, let's listen to our bodies and trust our own personal experiences. We can cultivate a far more balanced and respectful relationship with all aspects of our Environment, especially the Sun.

PHYSICAL CONTACT WITH NATURE

When was the last time you walked barefoot on bare earth? Maybe out in your backyard, at the park, or at the beach?

Have you noticed how much better you feel almost instantly?

When it comes to self-care that's easy and free, it just doesn't get much better than "Grounding." "Grounding" or "Earthing" is the practice of making physical contact with the Earth. Since electricity underlies all the biochemistry and physiology of our bodies, having adequate electrons from physical contact with the Earth has far reaching and important health benefits.

Sometimes I wonder: Are our ancestors looking down from above, laughing at us that something so free, so simple, and so natural is now a special "thing?"

For most of our evolutionary history, humans have had continuous contact with the Earth. Physical connection with the Earth was always part of our everyday life. Nowadays, our rubber soled shoes, asphalt, building materials and living environments have completely separated us from this physical contact with the Earth. Many of us, especially city dwellers, go for weeks, months, or years, without ever touching the Earth to properly ground our bodies.

The result is a chronic disturbance in the electrical flow in our bodies, which directly impacts our circulation and inflammatory levels, setting the stage for many modern inflammatory conditions. This is because energy and electricity underlies all the biochemistry in our human body.

Just as electrical appliances (like your refrigerator or washer-dryer) need to be plugged into the third-prong of the outlet to ground and minimize damage from short-circuiting, we humans need to be grounded for optimal functioning.

Research now tells us that Grounding can

- act as a powerful antioxidant, reducing free radical damage,
- decrease inflammation and pain,
- reduce stress levels,
- shift our nervous system into a more tranquil state,
- support healthy immune function,
- enhance cardiovascular health,
- improve circulation,
- promote better sleep,
- slow the aging process, and
- protect from the influence of EMF pollution on our health.[46] [47]

"Wow! All this from simply making physical contact with nature? I'm in! But how?"

SUPERWELLNESS RECIPE FOR GROUNDING/EARTHING

Studies have shown that in as little as two seconds of grounding, there are measurable benefits, such as change in our skin conductance, indicative of a nervous system that's more peaceful and tranquil. These benefits continue to increase and stabilize after about 45 minutes of grounding.[48]

- Dr. Edith recommends touching the earth daily, at least a few seconds each day. Of course 45 minutes is ideal.
- At least once a week, go to the beach, go to the park, or use your backyard to ground for a full 45 minutes.
- If you don't have easy access to yards, parks or beaches, you can purchase a grounding mat that plugs to the third prong of your outlet. Grounding mats can be found online. -OR- consider moving to a new environment where your lifestyle promotes regular grounding (as I did!).

There's a great deal of compelling research on the science behind grounding. I recommend reading the book *"Earthing: The Most Important Health Discovery Ever"* by Clint Ober and Dr. Stephen Sinatra, M.D.

Try it out! Ground every day this week, and see how amazing you can feel.

SUPERWELLNESS LAB - OPTIMIZING YOUR OVERALL ENVIRONMENT

Based on the information in this chapter, how can you adapt your daily Environment to resynchronize with nature's rhythms? How can you take advantage of the healing power of natural sunlight during the day, restful darkness at night, and physical contact with the earth?

- Schedule time to go outside and enjoy healthy doses of natural sunlight each day.
- Minimize the negative impact of artificial lighting on your health.
- Cultivate a relaxing evening routine to transition to sleep.
- Create an environment of restful darkness at night.
- Ground your body's electrical energy (via physical contact with nature, and/or using a grounding mat) on a daily basis.

Here are some examples of how other SuperWellness friends have incorporated the materials of this chapter.

SAMPLE DAY A - for early risers:

- AM: Wake up by Sunrise. Go outside and enjoy 10 seconds of Sunrise within the 45 minute window when the UV index is zero.
- Spend some time barefoot on bare-earth in your backyard or at a park.
- While outside, take advantage of the fresh air and do 20 deep breaths.
- Take your lunch break outside, go for a walk and get some sun. Take 20 deep breaths while outside.
- PM: start dimming the lights 1.5 - 2 hours before bed. Use your Gratitude Journal as part of your night-time relaxation routine.
- Sleep/rest in a completely dark environment for 8 hours, including 11pm - 3am.

SAMPLE DAY B - for those who sleep in:

- Perhaps you slept in past the Sunrise window.
- Take your lunch break outside, go for a walk and get some sun. Take 20 deep breaths while outside.
- Sunset: enjoy gazing at the Sunset for 10 seconds within the 45 minute window when the UV index is zero, preferably barefoot on bare-earth.

- PM: start dimming the lights 1.5 - 2 hours before bed. Use your Gratitude Journal as part of your night-time relaxation routine.
- Sleep/rest in a completely dark environment for 8 hours, including 11pm - 3am.

SAMPLE DAY C - Weekend or Free Days:

- Make it a priority to enjoy time in nature. E.g. a hike in the woods, a day at the beach, or a walk through the neighborhood park;
- Spend 45 minutes in physical contact with the earth, barefoot on bare-earth, use the time to read a book or write in your gratitude journal.
- Enjoy your 2 x 20 breaths + Qigong meridian patting while outside.
- Sleep/rest like a baby at night, 8 or more hours in complete darkness, including 11pm - 3am.

So simple and delicious! I hope that you feel excited about the power of these very small shifts to massively upgrade your energy, your health, and your life!

A full discussion about optimizing these key elements of our Environment (Light, Darkness, and Grounding) can be found in your book bonuses. Visit www.SuperWellness.com/BookBonuses/

As we conclude this chapter, I'd love to share with you a personal story about the power of optimizing my own living Environment.

THE MOST SURPRISING GIFTS OF ALL

In 2013, after returning to San Francisco from my Dark Room Retreat, I noticed some strange and remarkable changes.

During the dark retreat, without the use of my physical vision, I learned to see/sense/feel more strongly with my other senses. I expected this heightened sensitivity to be temporary and disappear after returning to my "normal" life. But even months after returning to my daily life in San Francisco, I noticed that the senses remained enhanced. I continued to see, sense, feel, smell, hear far stronger than ever before, just as in dark room.

This increased sensitivity was a great gift in my work with clients at the clinic, assisting in quicker diagnosis and more precise treatments. But at night, when it was time to sleep, I was acutely aware of the noises and mixed energies of the city.

Dark Room Retreat gave me a brand new reference point for the kind of deep stillness that is possible at night. Once I tasted this stillness, there was no turning back.

I was hungry for silence. Hungry for darkness. I craved the nourishment of nature.

So my amazing husband Dave let me convince him to move one-hour outside the city to the countryside, to live in a cute little cottage surrounded by trees, sunshine, and nature.

Now the thing is - all my life, I loved to sleep in. I was never a morning person. If you asked my husband, he'd say you should never talk to me in the morning without a strong cup of coffee first. If you asked my rowing teammates at Harvard, they'd tell you about all the times they had to bang on my dorm room window and wake me up, because I overslept morning team practice!

All my life, I loved to sleep in. I was never a morning person.

Shockingly, within the first month of moving to the countryside, I experienced myself bouncing out of bed, feeling bright and energized in the morning without coffee!

Living in the city, I used to "discipline" myself to go to bed at a decent hour because of the research-proven health benefits of sleep. Now living in the country, without city lights constantly stimulating me late into the night, I felt naturally relaxed and sleepy after the sun went down. I found myself tucking into bed at a "decent hour" without any willpower or discipline. Our new home had no street lights coming from outside, so our bedroom was naturally dark and conducive to deep restful sleep.

Finally, the deep restful sleep I first tasted in Dark Room Retreat was available every single night. Wow!

In the mornings, our east-facing windows let in the most beautiful Sunrise. I had no idea it could be so easy to wake up naturally and effortlessly. Often there's no need for an alarm and certainly no need to press the snooze button 20 times.

What a wonderful feeling it is to wake up consistently refreshed, happy and alive - without coffee!

Then after one month of living in nature, I noticed a change in my **fertility cycles**.

Being a "natural health nut", I had been tracking my cycles for years. All my adult life, my cycles had fluctuated between 32 to 35 days. The slight irregularity was never of medical concern. But now, with no other change in my lifestyle (same eating, same exercise, same job) except living in nature, the cycle synchronized perfectly to 28 days.

Month after month, my cycle stayed perfectly synchronized to the full moon and new moon.

Then, the greatest surprise of all.

Soon after moving to the countryside, I began to experience a series of beautiful dreams and meditations where the spirit of our baby boy appeared, sharing wisdom and messages to prepare for his conception. If this sounds strange to you, it was very strange to me too! At that time, David and I had not been planning to start a family yet. But through these dream encounters that repeated over many months, we fell in love with the spirit of our little boy.

We can't go back and do a double-blind placebo controlled study to compare. But I believe that living in nature, earthing and grounding regularly, enjoying full sunshine and full darkness, and being well-rested and inspired - influenced David's and my fertility in profound ways. It may have also enhanced our receptivity to subtle energies during dreamtime and meditations.

When David and I finally decided we were ready to conceive our boy, my cycles were so perfectly synchronized that we knew precisely my fertility window, without any devices like ovulation predictor kits or fertility tracking apps. Our boy was conceived on the very first "try." In a future book, I look forward to sharing the full story that led to the conscious conception of our child. While this may have been pure good luck (we certainly feel extremely lucky!), I believe that our living in the most health-promoting natural environment was amongst the key ingredients that blessed us with such incredible "luck" in the fertility department.

So beyond all the science-proven health benefits of

- sunshine during the day,
- darkness at night, and
- regular physical contact with nature,

could there be some additional benefits that are more subtle and magical?

What surprising gifts and blessings might unfold in **your** life, as you synchronize your energy systems back to nature's rhythms?

I'm excited for you to find out!

SUMMARY OF 'E' IS FOR ENVIRONMENT

In this chapter, we explored the keys to optimizing our Environment to feel Energized and Electrified! We discovered the massive health benefits that can come from the right doses of **Sunlight**, **Darkness**, and **Nature**.

One of my mentors Brendon Burchard often reminds us that *"Common sense is not common practice."* We cannot truly imagine the enormous benefits of these simple shifts, until we put them back into practice again.

As I study the scientific research on how these factors can influence our health, hormones, and metabolism in such dramatic ways, I often find myself wondering:

"How much of our medical research is based on studying subjects (human or animal) that aren't getting optimal Sunshine or sleeping in Darkness? Subjects whose Electricity is not properly grounded?"

"How much of our understanding of food, metabolism, and human health becomes obsolete if those environmental factors were optimized first?"

In my clinical experience, patients who implemented these simple environmental shifts experienced far reaching benefits, often reducing their dependence on previously rigid diet or exercise regimens.

For readers who are health researchers, I invite you to ask these curious questions together with me. Further studies are needed to understand how Environmental factors can impact more traditional approaches to health (like diet and exercise). There's so much more to learn.

Scientific studies aside, for me it was through direct experience that I came to see these "non-food" influences as true Essential Nutrients for life. E.g. Conscious Breathing, Gratitude Practice, Sunshine, Darkness, Contact with Nature, etc.. It is with direct personal experience that we can truly appreciate their power.

As always, experiment and test these out for yourself. Please share your experience with the SuperWellness community. There's much to learn together.

———————

At this moment, you might be wondering:

"Dr. Edith, surely you can't write a book about wellness without addressing diet and nutrition! I want to know what you think about Paleo vs. Vegan vs. Keto diets?"

You're right. It's time to talk about that!

"Dr. Edith, what is this fascinating new science about Light and Water? You said Water can act like a rechargeable solar battery? Our bodies may be like solar-powered hybrid vehicles? This is mind-blowing stuff. How does it work?"

Our journey just keeps getting better and better! When you're ready, turn the page and let's take it to a whole other level.

'H' was for coming Home to ourselves.

'E' was for optimizing our Environment.

Next up, 'A' is for Agua (water). 'A' is for *"Aaaaarmph!"* (food).

CHAPTER 5

'A' is for Agua, 'A' is for *"Aaaarmph!"*

"Water is the mirror that has the ability to show us what we cannot see. It's the blueprint for our reality, which can change with a single, positive thought."

~ Masaru Emoto ~

WHICH ONE FIRST?

Question for you:

When it comes to our Food and Water, which one is more important, if you had to choose?

"Oh, there you go again with your crazy questions, Dr. Edith. Do I have to choose?"

Remember in Chapter 3 when we compared the importance of Breathing vs. Water vs. Food from a pure survival perspective? I hope you still agree that Breathing is #1. Now when it comes to Food and Water, if you had to choose, which one is a higher priority?

*"Well, Dr. Edith, if you put it that way, **Water is the priority of course!** But what is there to know about Water? Just drink 64 ounces a day of H2O. End of story. Right?"*

It turns out there's fascinating new science about how water influences our health in surprising ways. It's cutting edge stuff that we never learned in school.

Get ready for a wild ride. This chapter is going to blow your socks off.

A IS FOR AGUA (WATER)

Water is the most fundamental substance to life on earth. It accounts for 60-75% of our body weight. But did you know that if we calculate on the basis of molecules, **99+% of the molecules in our human body is Water**? Scientists spend so much time studying how various other molecules work in our body. Shouldn't we spend more of our scientific resources to learn about Water?

In school, we were taught to see water as an inactive background medium upon which our biology and chemistry "just happens." But there are many strange properties of water that our textbooks never explained very well. For example, why does water have such high surface tension? Why does hot water freeze faster than cold water? Why does water have lower density when in a solid state than in the liquid state?

Fortunately for us, over the last two decades, groundbreaking scientific research is now painting a new story about how water works. It turns out that water is far more active and fascinating than we ever learned in school. This may have profound implications for our health and our planet.

Before we get into the mind-bending new science of water, let's start with the most practical and frequently asked questions first.

"How much water should I drink?"

"What kind of water should I drink?"

HOW MUCH WATER SHOULD I DRINK?

Should everyone be drinking "64 ounces" of water every day? I trust that by now, as a SuperWellness ninja-in-training, you're starting to laugh at these one-size-fits-all recommendations.

The truth is that we're all different. Our hydration needs depend on many factors. E.g.: your level of activity, did you sweat a lot that day, do you live in a hot and dry desert-like environment vs. a more damp environment, did you eat plenty of watery fruits and veggies or did you have some foods that may be drying or dehydrating, etc.. Also some medications, herbs or supplements can influence our water needs.

Perhaps the real question we should be asking is - **how do I know if I am properly hydrated?**

Yes, bingo! **By listening to the body.** We drink when we're thirsty and observe the color and frequency of urination.

Do you pay attention to the color and frequency of your urine?

When we're well-hydrated, our urine looks clear-ish pale yellow and relatively copious. (Note: Red beets and some vitamins can influence the color.) It's normal to urinate 4x to 10x in one day. If you find that your urine is a very dark color and scant in quantity, then it's likely that you're dehydrated and need more water. If you're urinating more than 10x in one day, this is considered frequent urination. It may be a sign of diabetes / pre-diabetes, or other medical conditions involving the kidney or bladder. Please consult your doctor to rule out anything that requires medical attention.

For most normal healthy adults, drinking the quantity of water that yields clear-ish pale yellow urine, and urinating about 5-8x per day, will likely mean that you're drinking enough water.

Rather than the one-size-fits-all "64 ounces per day" recommendation, let us listen to our bodies. It's time to bring back this type of self-awareness in our world again. Yes?

Now onto the more interesting and slightly controversial question.

WHAT KIND OF WATER SHOULD I DRINK?

Should we drink tap water? Filtered water? Spring water? Reverse osmosis? Distilled? So many choices it's dizzying!

First, I invite all of us to take a pause and give thanks to this blessed life where we have a choice of so many potable waters. In far too many communities around the globe, people do not have access to <u>any</u> clean drinking water. So what an incredible luxury for us to not just have one type of drinkable water, but a choice of several types of water. It's a profound gift not to be taken lightly.

Now… given that we do have a choice, let's choose wisely so that we can be as healthy and vibrant as possible! Let's use our added vitality and energy to create a better world where everybody can enjoy a healthy life! Yes? Can I get an amen-allelujah-aho on this one?

So what kind of water should we drink?

Short answer: the cleanest, tastiest, purest water that you can access!

I generally choose (in order of preference):

1) the best quality real **Spring Water** that I can get which comes in a glass bottle (not plastic),

2) **Reverse Osmosis Water** (purchased at the health food store or purified with an at-home Reverse Osmosis device) or **Distilled Water** (through a water distillation device)

3) **Tap Water filtered** with the highest quality filtration device that can remove the most contaminants.

For Reverse Osmosis Water or Distilled Water, I recommend adding back healthy minerals using a tiny pinch of Himalayan Pink Salt or Celtic Sea Salt in each glass. Later in this chapter, I will also discuss why we may like to "vortex" or "charge up" the water to give it more "life force" before consuming. *Note: If you have a health condition where careful dosing of salts and minerals are of medical concern, please be sure to consult your healthcare provider for professional guidance.*

"Wait a minute, Dr. Edith. **What about regular (unfiltered) Tap Water?"**

Personally, I drink unfiltered Tap Water only when there is no other choice available. There are a number of reasons that our municipal tap water concerns me. Fortunately, there are now great water filtration devices that can remove most (if not all) the major contaminants.

As more of us become educated about these important issues, I hope that we can come together as a community to ensure that everyone can enjoy pure clean water, fresh out of the tap. If we can put satellites into space and make iPhones with thousands of features, surely we can put our energy into creating cleaner water for everyone. Don't you agree?

Here are the top reasons why I choose not to drink (unfiltered) Tap Water if there's a choice:

- **Chlorine.** Municipal water systems receive their water from a variety of sources. Many are closed-loop systems where wastewater is recycled, filtered and sanitized. To kill pathogens, Chlorine is added as a necessary disinfectant. I invite you to do a quick web search on "Chlorine water health effects" and decide the pros and cons for yourself.[49] *(Note: Bottled water generally tastes better than tap water because it's disinfected with other methods like Micron filtration, Ozone, UV, and not Chlorine.)*

- **Fluoride.** In the U.S., about 70% of public water systems have added Fluoride. Around the world, most industrialized nations now ban water fluoridation.[50] Here in the U.S, we've been told that fluoride is good for our teeth. But it turns out this refers to topical application and not oral ingestion. For me, it's hard to understand putting any un-prescribed medication into drinking water, where infants, the elderly, pregnant women are all given doses in uncontrolled quantities. Also, there's debate over why the fluoride in our tap water comes from a toxic industrial pollutant (from the phosphate fertilizer industry), rather than the form of fluoride normally found in nature.

  Because this can be a controversial topic, I recommend for everyone to research and decide for themselves. The Fluoride Action Network website offers a great library of resources to learn more.[51] For a deeper dive, you might find the book *"The Fluoride Deception"* by Christopher Bryson to be valuable.

- **Fluoride & Chlorine may affect your Iodine absorption**? Do you remember from high-school chemistry class that Fluorine (F), Chlorine (Cl), Bromine (Br), and Iodine (I) are all in the same column on the periodic table? This means F, Cl, Br can block the absorption of Iodine, a critical nutrient for our health, especially for our **thyroid.** *As you know, this book does not diagnose or treat any medical conditions. If you have a history of hypothyroidism, please continue to work closely with your doctor.* I recommend to also educate yourself on how to lower your exposure to Fluoride, Chlorine, and Bromine.

- **Drugs your doctor did not prescribe for you.** In a 2008 report by the Associated Press, pharmaceutical drugs were found in the tap water of the majority of metropolitan areas in the U.S..[52] This means many of us are unwittingly taking low doses of many medications by drinking Tap Water. These included antibiotics, blood pressure medication, hormones, and antidepressant drugs. A 2013 EPA study confirmed the issue, with opioids, acid-reflux medications, and blood pressure medications at the top of the list.[53]

- **Other contaminants:** Get your rotten tomatoes ready. This one could make you want to throw them at me. A recent study found plastic contaminants in 83% of world-wide tap water systems and in 94% of U.S. tap water.[54] A large-scale study by Environmental Working Group (EWG) found a variety of toxic chemicals in the U.S. tap water system. For example: nearly two-thirds Americans have tap water that contain unsafe levels of Hexavalent Chromium (the chemical that Erin Brockovich warned us about).[55] Yikes!

  For readers in the U.S., the EWG has a phenomenal database for looking up data on Tap Water in your zip code.

  www.ewg.org/tapwater/ I recommend highly.

Many SuperWellness readers are already long time health-nuts. So perhaps you were already aware of these issues with our tap water system. If this is your first time hearing such news, you are probably in shock as I was when I first learned of all this.

The truth is, these contaminants shouldn't be in our water. But at the time of this writing, they are. So it's up to each of us to respond wisely. It is only with knowledge that we can empower ourselves to make the best choices for ourselves and our families.

So what now? Can you do some research and invest in the most high quality water filtration system that your family can access? Can you shift your grocery budgets and start getting Spring Water or Reverse Osmosis water from your local health food store? Or will you subscribe to a Spring Water delivery service for your home and office?

Surely we can all agree that having healthy water is key to long-term health for you and your family.

SUPERWELLNESS LAB - RESEARCH YOUR LOCAL WATER OPTIONS

For your SuperWellness Lab, spend an hour or two this week to research about the water options in your local area.

- Try various brands of bottled Spring Water (preferably in glass) that you have available in your area.
- Check with your local health food store for their water options.
- If you're in the U.S., check the EWG website for water contaminants found in your zip code (www.ewg.org/tapwater). Then do an online search to learn about the various water purifications devices available to filter out the contaminants specific to your local tap water system.
- My favorite water filtration devices are listed in your book bonuses. www.SuperWellness.com/BookBonuses/
- What are the top 3 purest water options available to you?

Drinking pure clean water is one of the best investments that we can make on our health, energy, and vitality. I feel confident you'll find it well worth the effort!

Celebrate! That's the end of the serious stuff. **Now let's focus on the fun part!**

MINDBLOWING NEW DISCOVERIES ABOUT WATER

Did you know that scientists have discovered Water can hold memory and information, like a liquid-crystal computer? And this information changes the structure of water, which may influence how the water hydrates or transports nutrients?

Did you know that Water can be charged up by light like a rechargeable solar battery, and this electricity drives much of our physiology?

"Whoa Whoa Whoa. Slow down, Dr. Edith! You're blowing my mind. Water has memory?"

Yes. Water has memory!

There's an excellent documentary called *"Water: The Great Mystery"* that I encourage everybody to watch. One of the scientists featured in the documentary is Dr. Masaru Emoto, who pioneered this field by showing the world that water may have the ability to hold memory, like a liquid-crystal computer!

Have you heard of Dr. Emoto? Or seen his water crystal photos?

His inquiry began with the question: *Why is it that no two snowflakes ever look alike? What determines the snowflake's structure? Does human consciousness influence the geometry in any way?*

In his lab, he flash-froze different samples of water and took high resolution photos of the water crystals as they're thawing. He experimented with exposing the bottles of water to different labels. Some were labeled with positive messages like "Love," "Thank You," and "Gratitude," etc., and others were labeled with negative messages like "I hate you," or "You make me sick," etc.. He would flash-freeze the water and then photograph the different water crystals as they were thawing.

The results were stunning.

When he exposed water molecules to information of love, kindness, gratitude, and appreciation, the water crystals formed beautiful and symmetrical patterns. But when water was exposed to messages of anger or hatred, the water crystals formed chaotic, ugly or asymmetrical arrangements, or no pattern at all. He also did experiments exposing some water samples to Mozart and Beethoven vs. Heavy Metal music and found interesting differences.

While some might argue the objective scientific rigor of Dr. Emoto's experiments, his discoveries burst open our minds to fascinating new possibilities. It invited many scientists to take a brand new look at what water is, and how it works.

As water scientists around the world began to discover fascinating new properties of water, including those featured in the *"Water: A Great Mystery"* documentary, a new terminology emerged. Water that creates a symmetrical hexagonal structure is called **"structured water."** Water that creates a chaotic and asymmetrical pattern is called **"unstructured water."** Over time, scientists discovered a variety of ways to "structurize" the water, with exciting possible applications in agriculture and health.

Have you noticed that water naturally moves in curves and vortexes in nature? This vortexing movement has been found to (re)structurize water. But our modern day city water systems push our water through 90-degree pipes, which according to the documentary, can break up the water clusters and create "unstructured water."

Here's the part of the documentary that most caught my attention. Agricultural experiments were conducted where one half of the field was watered using "unstructured tap water," while the other half was watered using "structurized water." The two sides of the field had the same soil nutrient composition, same sunshine, same seeds; the only difference was the structure of the water. The results were incredible!

The half of the field that was watered using structurized water was **hydrated using 30% less total water!** The overall **yield was higher** with the structured water. The fruits and vegetables grew bigger, stronger, healthier, and found to have higher overall nutrient density.

Does this mean that more food can be produced with less water if we simply vortex and structurize the water first?

Furthermore, if structured water had a stronger hydrating effect on plants, could it also have a similar impact in the human body? What if the structure also determines how effectively nutrients are transported in our human body, not just in the plants?

What if?

This *"Water: A Great Mystery"* documentary is fascinating. I cannot recommend it highly enough. My favorite study by Dr. Emoto is where he flash-froze highly contaminated dirty waters and found ugly and asymmetrical unstructured water. Then after exposing the contaminated water to prayers of love, healing, and harmony, the water crystals became stunningly clear, symmetrical, and beautiful.

The beauty of the water crystals were breathtaking.

It's an important reminder that **our human consciousness may be far more powerful than we realized.**

As we shared in Chapter 1, studies suggest that eating and drinking under a stressful emotional state can have negative effects on our health. Could it be that the "structure" of water in our body is influenced by our emotional states, which then changes how the water functions in our body?

Is it possible that positive emotions "structurize" our water molecules, such that nutrients can transport more efficiently, allowing our physiology to function more optimally?

Is this why most traditional cultures recommend saying a prayer or taking a moment of gratitude before consuming a meal?

Like you, I'm a curious person with many questions and look forward to continuing the learning as these scientific discoveries unfold.

*"Wow! Dr. Edith, this is amazing stuff! What about that idea of **water acting like a rechargeable solar battery** that you mentioned in the last chapter?*

Yes! Such an exciting time in which we live. I can hardly contain myself either!

There's a pioneering scientist at University of Washington named **Professor Gerald Pollack**. He published a book called *"**The Fourth Phase** of Water." Dr. Pollack discovered that water can act like a rechargeable battery. It turns out this special electrical property drives much of our cellular physiology, such as the contraction and relaxation cycles of muscles and the folding and unfolding of protein molecules.

When the water in our cells have enough charge, our physiology can work optimally. With too little charge, many physiological functions may fall short.

I know some of this may sound a little crazy. So before you assume that I'm hallucinating on some mind-altering drugs, bear with me, my friend. This is really good stuff you don't want to miss!

WATER HAS FOUR PHASES? WATER STORES ENERGY LIKE A BATTERY?

Let's start with the basics. When we were in school, what did they tell us about Water and its different phases?

"Water has three phases: 1) gas/vapor, 2) liquid phase, and 3) solid phase (ice). Right?"

Professor Gerald Pollack and his colleagues discovered that this is not entirely true. It turns out that **water has a Fourth Phase, with fascinating electrical activities that drives much of our cellular physiology**, none of which we learned about in chemistry or biology classes!

According to Dr. Pollack's book and online videos, there are several key characteristics of this Fourth Phase of Water that we should all know about:

- It's a special phase that exists between Ice and Liquid. When liquid water is about to freeze and turn into ice, it changes to this "Fourth Phase" as an intermediary. Likewise, when ice is melting back into liquid water, it goes into this "Fourth Phase" as intermediary;

- In this special state, it pushes out all contaminants, so Professor Pollack calls it the "Exclusion Zone", aka "**EZ Water**";

- Note: Dr. Pollack's lab is already using this mechanism to develop a "filterless water filter" by collecting the EZ Water! *Wow, what a brilliant and EZ solution (ha!).*

- It turns out that EZ Water (or Fourth Phase Water) is not actually H2O! This water is **H3O2**.

- EZ Water stores electrical energy like a rechargeable battery;

- Light charges up the energy in water to create more EZ Water;

- Dr. Pollack's team has already created the first usable **Solar Water Battery** using this rechargeable battery feature of water!

- **EZ Water is fundamental to all our cellular function and a key driver of our blood circulation.**

According to Dr. Pollack's research, while we all need regular "bulk" water for hydration, it is by increasing the amount of EZ Water that we can energize our cellular physiology to function more optimally.

So what are some ways that can potentially increase your body's EZ Water, based on Dr. Pollack and his team's experiments?

- Getting adequate Sunlight (mmm, sound familiar?);

- Fresh Juices (because we're drinking the water inside the plant's cell, which is already EZ water);

- Increasing your Oxygenation levels (because H2O needs extra O's to become H3O2);

- A variety of natural health supplements have been found to increase EZ in his experiments;

- Infrared heat (such as from sun, sauna, and even snuggling with loved ones, puppies and kittens, etc.) could all theoretically increase EZ Water. *Remember our chapter 1 on non-food nourishment?*

- Vortexing our water may help increase EZ water. [56]

I wonder: is it possible that the Cold/Ice therapy, as in the Wim Hof Method, helps by increasing our exposure to EZ Water? This is in addition to the increased Oxygenation in Wim Hof Method which may also enhance EZ Water.

These new findings about water are revolutionizing our understanding of biology and physiology. I believe in the next 10 to 20 years, many of our textbooks will be entirely rewritten to shift into a brand new understanding of water, biology and health.

Dr. Gerald Pollack is a brilliant, entertaining, fun, and dynamic speaker with a great gift for translating cutting edge science into lay-person friendly terms. He's a true pioneer. I'm a huge fan of his work and encourage you to read his book *"The Fourth Phase of Water"* and follow his online lectures and interviews.

"Wow, Dr. Edith! This is some mind-blowing futuristic stuff. I just totally dropped my kale smoothie on the floor. But how do I actually apply all of this to my life?"

SUPERWELLNESS LAB - PLAY WITH SUPERCHARGING YOUR WATER

This is new science, so there's much we don't fully know yet. I encourage you to play with your water and just have fun!

In addition to researching the cleanest, purest water available, you can also experiment with structurizing your water by

- spinning it in a special "vortexing" device,
- simply stirring it before drinking,
- playing music to your water,
- sending positive intentions to your water, and/or
- putting kind and loving words on your water containers.

Invite your friends and family to do a blind taste test with you, and see if you can taste/feel the difference. You may notice a different texture or mouthfeel as other SuperWellness participants have noticed in our classes.

If "talking to your water" feels a little too "hokey" to you, then focus on increasing your *EZ water* based on Dr. Gerald Pollack's research findings in the above section. E.g.

- drink plenty of fresh clean water,
- vortex your water,
- make sure you get adequate doses of sunlight and oxygen, and
- use the other tips as listed in the section above on EZ Water.

Find out if you feel more energized by increasing your EZ Water in these ways.

Note: About 15 years ago, I had a Chinese Medicine Professor who recommended drinking a specially made **lukewarm water using a mixture of 50% boiling water and 50% ice-cubes.** *He said it could "Harmonize the Yin and Yang" of our body. I had no idea about EZ water back then. Could this be a way to make a great cup of EZ Water?*

Recently, I have been drinking this 50-50 "yin-yang" water every mornings and feeling super! The skeptical scientist in me says it may be pure placebo, but I'm having lots of fun. Perhaps you might like to try?

All these experiments are low-risk, easy (EZ!), harmless, and fun. I encourage you to give them a try and decide for yourself.

Congratulations! You now know more about water than the vast majority of the world!

Are you ready for a snack break? After our epic tour with Breathing, Gratitude, Sunlight, Darkness, Grounding and Water, now we finally make a pit stop for Food. 'A' is for *"Aaaarmph!"*

But what to eat?

'A' IS FOR *AAAARMPH!* (FOOD)

*"There are only three things that women need:
food, water, and compliments. That's right. And an
occasional pair of shoes."*

~ *Chris Rock* ~

Here's the thing: Food should be a source of joy, deliciousness and vitality, but our society has made it a source of enormous stress and confusion for so many of us.

No surprise, because since the 80s, our understanding of "what to eat, what not to eat" has gone topsy-turvy. Many of us grew up with the USDA "Four Food Groups." Then came the USDA Food Pyramid in 1992, which got massively overhauled in 2005. More recently in 2011, the Food Pyramid was thrown out and replaced by a colorful plate showing five food groups.[57]

As for popular diets, like so many of us, I too have experimented with my fair share of programs over the years. Many of us try one diet and get short-term results. Then we lose discipline or willpower and fall off the bandwagon. A few months later we get back on the bandwagon, or we decide to dabble in a different diet.

Sometimes we just have to laugh at ourselves. Remember how in the 80s, people went fat-free and got fatter? We loaded ourselves with sugar, and all the obesity-related conditions skyrocketed. We've been reeling ever since.

Maybe we tried the Low Carb Diet. Maybe we tried the Zone Diet, the Atkins Diet, the South Beach Diet, the Macrobiotic Diet, the Acid-Alkaline Diet, or the Blood Type Diet. Nowadays many people are going Plant-based, Vegetarian, Vegan, or Raw, while others are debating between the Paleo vs. Ketogenic diet. And have you heard about the Specific Carbohydrate Diet, or Low-Fodmap diet, or the Lectin-free diet?

Which one is right for you? Maybe all of these? Maybe none of these?

Have you tried them all? Or do you just want to throw your hands in the air and give up?

Well I have a special treat for you!

I'm going to share with you a simple, powerful, and timeless approach to food that will eliminate all the confusion and anxiety.

This approach will either **make all future diets obsolete** -OR- it will **make your diet truly work for you the way you want**. Are you ready?

Drumroll....

It's called **the SuperWellness F.A.N. Diet.**

The F.A.N. Diet has only 3 simple rules.

1) Your food should be F̲un & Tasty!

2) Your food should make you feel A̲live!

3) Your food should cause N̲o N̲egative Effects!

That's it! If your diet fulfills all three rules, then I'm a FAN. If it breaks any of these three rules, I'm not a fan.

RULE #1: FOOD SHOULD BE FUN!

Your food and eating should be fun, joyful, and tasty. And I'm very serious about this!

In Chapter 1, we shared a study which suggested that eating under stress can override the beneficial effects of a "healthy" diet. We also know that when our physiology is in the "fight or flight" mode of stress, our salivary glands produce less digestive enzymes and our stomach and intestines receive less blood flow.

Remember that healthy nutrition is not just what we eat, but what we're able to digest and assimilate. Even if we eat the most healthy nutritious foods, it still needs to digest well. **When we eat in a state of fun and joy, we digest better!** If we eat in the state of stress, all our digestive function is suppressed.

I often tell patients: *"If you don't digest well, all this nice organic foods just makes very expensive poop!"*

From time to time, we all need a reminder to have fun, don't you agree? Food is meant to be fun and delicious! If we get still, slow down, and listen to our body, our taste buds will tell us powerful information about the optimal nutrition that the body wants or doesn't want.

For example, many women crave chocolate during pre-menstrual time because we're deficient in Magnesium, and we are craving it. Did you know that Cacao is the highest Magnesium-rich food on the planet? A nice piece of organic raw, dark chocolate may be the perfect medicine at that moment.

Rejoice! We can eat Chocolate!

Here's another example: there's a test we use at the clinic called the "Zinc Taste Test" to determine if patients are deficient in zinc. Patients drink a sip of a precisely diluted solution of zinc suspended in H2O. When patients are deficient zinc, this diluted solution of zinc tastes like a very pleasant water! On the other hand, if they're not deficient, then it tastes very unpleasant. There's almost an instant scowl on their face! So if we're willing to listen, the body will tell us what it needs or doesn't need.

At the end of the day, when it comes to healthy eating, if the food is not fun and tasty, what are the chances that we will stick with a certain healthy "diet?" Over the last few decades, we've all seen enough short-term fad diets come and go, don't you agree? So let's find a long-term plan that is fun and sustainable for the rest of our lives.

Let's find a plan that will never go out of style!

Rule #1: Fun.

RULE #2: YOUR FOOD SHOULD MAKE YOU FEEL ALIVE!

This is a simple, sensible, yet very advanced rule which requires learning to listen to our bodies' response after we eat.

For example, if we have a "food coma" after we eat, it's likely that our food is requiring too much energy to digest. Have you had this experience?

If we feel alive, energized, and vibrant in a stable and sustained way, then very likely the food is harmonious to our well-being and digesting well!

Remember how Dr. Pollack says that he believes we feel good drinking fresh juices because the plant cell water contains high concentrations of EZ Water. When we drink fresh live juice, it increases our own EZ Water, which charges up our cellular energy. **When our foods and drinks give us good energy, there's an <u>Aliveness</u> that we can all feel.**

It's a simple, timeless practice of paying attention, being present, and listening to the body. Our body is always telling us what it wants and what it doesn't want. The question is whether we're willing to listen.

Does your food make you feel Alive?

RULE #3: NO NEGATIVE EFFECTS!

This one is the most obvious. If a food causes a negative effect, such as an allergic reaction, then don't eat it!

However, the reason this simple rule is often overlooked is because we may have **low-grade or delayed inflammatory response** to certain foods. This can take some effort to sort out. Many of us have been living with low-grade food sensitivities all our lives. We don't truly know how much better we can feel, until we experiment with an elimination diet. For this reason, I'm a fan (F.A.N.!) of elimination systems like Melissa Hartwig's Whole 30, or Dr. Mark Hyman's The UltraSimple Diet, or Dr. Alejandro Junger's Clean Program, etc. just to name a few. There are many other great systems available.

I also encourage you to work with a professional healthcare provider and/or holistic nutritionist for food allergy testing as appropriate.

After eliminating common allergens or inflammatory ingredients, we have a new reference point for how great we can feel. We can gradually re-introduce one item at a time to experiment. Empowered by this better understanding of how our bodies feel with or without certain foods, we can make wiser choices about our long-term consumption (or elimination) of those items.

It's worth noting that many participants tell us that, **because of the holistic 360° nature of SuperWellness, food cravings often vanish naturally.** Practices like breathwork, gratitude, sunshine, darkness, grounding and hydration support our health in profound ways. People naturally eat less of the junky or inflammatory foods, without effort, discipline or willpower. So I invite you to this exciting new possibility!

When it comes to foods that cause "Negative effects", I have found five big offenders that cause the vast majority of issues amongst my patients.

Based on my experience, the five foods that cause the most irritation or inflammation are:

1) <u>"Frankenfood" Ingredients</u>

Always read labels and research ingredients that are highly processed or have strange chemical names. There are many processed or artificial substances that have been added to our foods that are highly questionable in my opinion. E.g.: aspartame, MSG, carrageenan, artificial preservatives, dyes and pesticides. Personally, I choose Organic whenever possible. Until the science demonstrates greater clarity about GMO safety, I try to avoid GMO foods, especially GMO soy and corn.

2) <u>Hydrogenated Oils or Oxidized Rancid Oils, Caution with High Heat</u>

Avoid all Hydrogenated Oils or Partially-hydrogenated Oils, also known as "Trans Fats." (We can say that Hydrogenated Oil is really a Frankenfood and belongs in the previous category.) When it comes to cooking, use oils that have high flash points and don't oxidize easily. My favorite oils for cooking are Coconut Oil and Grapeseed Oil. Because many oils oxidize easily when exposed to heat, it's best to drizzle on at the end and avoid cooking the oils at high heat.

3) <u>Milk and Dairy Products</u>

Milk (and dairy products) is likely the single most mucous producing and allergenic substance I've seen across the board in all my years of practice. To date, I have not seen patient's inflammatory or mucous-related symptoms not improve noticeably when milk is eliminated. (Examples include digestive, skin, joint or breathing symptoms.)

"But don't we need Milk for our health?" It's worth noting that 75% of humans are lactose intolerant after age 5. In some studies, the casein

protein in Milk has been found to be a possible carcinogen.[58] As for bone health, it turns out that countries with the highest Milk consumptions also have the highest osteoporosis rates.[59]

So I invite you to do some further research and experiment to find out for yourself. Join us for a future SuperWellness course, where we can explore together at length. There's always a lively discussion around this topic, with many questions and myths busted (e.g.: Doesn't milk build strong bones? Where else can I get calcium? What is actually in a bottle of milk? How is milk made, and what are possible environmental impacts? etc.).

4) Wheat & Gluten

Most readers of this book are familiar with Wheat-free or Gluten-free eating. Dr. William Davis, author of *"Wheat Belly,"* popularized the idea that when we hybridized our wheat plant in the U.S. to create a higher yield "dwarf wheat," it became much more allergenic and inflammatory. More recently, Dr. Stephen Gundry and his book *"The Plant Paradox"* introduced the idea that plants like Wheat have Lectins, the plant's natural defense system against pests or "predators," and it is the Lectins causing the inflammatory reaction in our bodies. Anthony William, author of *"Medical Medium,"* believes that Wheat may be feeding unresolved pathogens or viruses in our system, which creates added stress on our immune system.

Whatever the reason may be, the majority of my patients report improved mood and mental focus, better energy, decreased aches and pains, clearer skin, and better digestion after eliminating wheat (and gluten). Again I invite you to research and test it out for yourself.

5) Sugar

Sugar in small quantities and in its natural form is not inherently bad of course, it's just that the food industry adds large quantities sugar into nearly everything. The average American consumes about 22 teaspoons of sugar per day, or 77 pounds per year! [60] Chronically high levels of sugar creates sludgy blood circulation, leading way to "diabesity" and promoting a whole slew of inflammatory complications. Sugar has also been found to feed harmful bacteria, bad yeast, fungus, and cancer cells. Decreasing our intake of excessive sugars is one of the best gifts we can all give ourselves to create optimal health.

"Dr. Edith, honestly I already knew most of this stuff. But what can I eat in place of these?"

For Milk replacement, experiment with Organic Almond Milk, Organic Cashew Milk, Organic Coconut Milk, Organic Rice Milk, or Organic Non-GMO Soy Milk. Find the ones that are most fun and tasty for you!

For Wheat replacement, try rice or sweet potatoes instead of wheat. Spaghetti squash is a delicious and nutritious replacement for wheat pasta spaghetti. When it comes to gluten-free breads and baked goods, read the label to ensure that they are not filled with added sugar.

As for Sugar replacement, I like to keep all forms of added sugars to a minimum. (At my house, we do enjoy plenty of fresh organic fruits.) For sweeteners, try local raw organic honey or raw coconut sugar, which has a delicious mineral-rich taste. Instead of adding sugar to cooking or dessert recipes, I often add dates for sweetness.

In your new F.A.N. diet, I recommend enjoying a **colorful rainbow** diversity of fresh fruits and vegetables that are tasty, fun and nutrient dense. Have plenty of colorful berries and fresh greens. As a holistic practitioner, I spent thousands of hours studying many systems of nutrition. Ultimately, I found that the easiest way to cover a full spectrum of nutrients is to simply "eat the rainbow."

SUPERWELLNESS LAB - FINDING YOUR F.A.N. DIET

Are you a F.A.N. of your foods?

Please observe your eating this week, and ask yourself after every meal:

- Is this **F**un and tasty?
- Does this food make me feel **A**live and energized in a sustained way?
- Does this food cause **N**o **N**egative effects?

Go to your book bonuses and watch a lively discussion about the F.A.N. diet. www.SuperWellness.com/BookBonuses/ .

Experiment with the recommendations in this chapter. Become a F.A.N. of your diet again!

SUMMARY OF 'A' IS FOR AGUA, 'A' IS FOR *"AAAARMPH!"*

In this chapter, we shared a huge treasure-trove of healthy living tools. We developed a brand new appreciation for our water and food.

On Water (Agua), we learned about:

- what types of water to drink,
- how much water to drink,
- the new science about water's structure, memory, and consciousness,
- "The Fourth Phase of Water" (aka "EZ Water"), and
- how to increase the EZ Water in our body.

On Food (*Aaaarmph!*), we explored:

- a new timeless principle for healthy eating,
- your new F.A.N. diet,
- eating the rainbow, and
- the top 5 foods that may cause negative effects.

Congratulations, my friend! You're officially at the midway point of your H.E.A.L.T.H. journey. It is clear that you are truly committed to your health and well-being.

You are amazing!

We covered a lot of ground, so I invite you to take your time to integrate. Optimizing your hydration and finding your personal F.A.N. diet is a lifelong journey.

For a deeper dive into "Agua & Aaarmph!", be sure to take advantage of your book bonuses: www.SuperWellness.com/BookBonuses/ and share your experience with our online community.

When you're ready, our next chapter is everybody's favorite module on the H.E.A.L.T.H. journey.

- 'H' was for coming Home.

- 'E' was for Environment.

- 'A' was for Agua and *Aaaarmph!*

Now 'L' is for Lightening Up on all levels. We'll learn how to get back more time and create more spaciousness in our lives again. Find out why 'L' is everybody's favorite module.

CHAPTER 6
'L' is for Lightening Up

"Empty your cup so that it may be filled.
Become devoid to gain totality."

~ Bruce Lee ~

LESS IS MORE; SLOWER IS FASTER

Have you ever heard the Zen parable called *"The Faster The Slower?"*

The story goes that an eager student treks up the mountains to study the art of sword-fighting under a great master.

The student meets the teacher: 'Master, if I study diligently, how long will it take to learn the skills of sword-fighting?'

Teacher says: '10 years perhaps.'

Student: 'My father is an old man, and I must return to look after him. What if I work exceptionally hard then how long will it take me?'

Teacher: 'In that case, it will probably take 30 years.'

Student: '!'

'First you said 10 years and now you say 30. Look, I'm willing to suffer any kind of hardship and sacrifice! I just want to learn it in the shortest time possible!"

Teacher: 'In that case, you'll have to study with me for 70 years.'

Student: '!'

If we take our time, we'll achieve our goals faster than if we hurry."

(From *"Zen Speaks: Shouts of Nothingness"* by Tsai Chih Chung & Brian Bruya.)[61]

Life is full of paradoxes like this, isn't it? There are many situations where, if we take our time, we can achieve our goals faster than if we rush.

How often do we pause and consider if "Less is More" and "Slower is Faster?"

HOW WE EAT VS. WHAT WE EAT

At my clinic, we've seen countless patients who eat the best healthy organic foods. They take all the best supplements, yet their clinical presentation and lab tests still show signs of **nutrient deficiencies.** After working with thousands of patients, I've come to appreciate that healthy nutrition is not just about **"what we eat"** but also **"how we eat."** Shifting the "how" part may be exactly what we need to turn our health around.

The truth is, many people in our community are already "health nuts" who eat the best foods, but we don't always digest or assimilate the food very well. We eat under stress. We eat on the run. Sometimes we 'snarf' down a whole lunch in a few minutes while rushing to meet our deadlines at the computer. When we suffer from digestive upset, we immediately wonder: *"What did I eat?"*

What if... the issue here is not the "what", but the "how?"

Could something as simple as slowing down, savoring our food, and chewing more - be the perfect antidote?

"Dr. Edith, that sounds nice. But you don't understand. I have a very high pressured job. There's not much time for lunch. When I get home in the evening, we have to do dinner quickly, so the kids can finish their homework and get to bed at a decent hour. We can't slow down. There's not enough time in the day."

I hear you. Many of us are in a similar predicament. Our community is filled with incredible high achievers: successful professionals, supermoms, superdads, elite athletes and brilliant entrepreneurs. We're all striving for greater productivity and efficiency. But just like in the Zen story, life is full of paradoxes.

When my patients cultivate the practice of slowing down, chewing more, savoring each meal mindfully, they consistently tell me how much better they feel in their mind, body, and spirit. When we eat slower, we feel more satiated. We enjoy more and naturally eat less. The food tastes so much more delicious, and we digest much better.

We have more energy and mental clarity, and our productivity skyrockets!

Sometimes taking 15-20 minutes extra to slow down and enjoy our food in a peaceful way can give us <u>hours</u> of extra productivity in the day. So if you feel you don't have enough time in the day, slowing down may be exactly what you need.

From a physiological perspective, when we eat in a rush without chewing properly, the body has a hard time digesting and assimilating the meal. Our salivary glands do not produce digestive enzymes when we're under stress, and every aspect of our digestive function is suppressed. Of course, if we don't digest the food well, we won't assimilate the nutrients. Rather than feeling nourished and energized by the food, our body and mind becomes more sluggish.

Eating like this is the opposite of efficient.

That's why I remind patients: *"If your food is not digested well or assimilated, it makes very expensive poop!"*

So we can say that eating in a rush the way most of us eat is quite wasteful.

Let's find a better way.

MINDFUL EATING IS FUN AND ECONOMICAL!

I first discovered the magic of **mindfulness eating practice** after quitting my software job, downsizing massively, and moving into my boyfriend (now husband) David's minimalist 8ft x 8ft room.

Living in pricey San Francisco with little-to-no income meant that we had to get very creative with our budget. Sometimes we ate rice and beans. But often, it was just a simple bowl of rice with a little seasoning.

One day, I came across a book by Thich Nhat Hanh called *"Anger."* In it, he explained how eating too much too fast, and eating under stress, can contribute to the arising of anger. He pointed out many benefits of slowing down and eating more mindfully. Since David and I were living so frugally, I was especially drawn to the idea that slowing down and savoring our food might be good for our budget.

Mindful Eating could save us big moola!

Here's an excerpt from Thich Nhat Hanh's book:

*"Our eyes are bigger than our stomach. We have to empower our eyes with the energy of mindfulness so that we know exactly what amount of food we really need. [...] **If you can eat like that, you can afford to buy less. When you buy less food, you can afford to buy organically grown food."** [62]*

David and I had no budget for date nights out at fancy restaurants. So we decided to try mindfulness eating practice at home, with a simple bowl of rice and beans, for our romantic "date-nights."

We sat together cross-legged on the floor facing one another, each with a simple bowl. As inspiration and guidance, we took turns reading Thich Nhat Hanh's book out loud for one another. As we ate, we chewed every bite 30 times, 50 times, even 100 times, until the food was liquefied.

Wow. The intensely delicious flavors were unimaginable! I had no idea a simple bowl of rice and beans could taste so amazing.

From time to time, we would pause and share what we were experiencing. But most of the time we were silent, chewing and enjoying the flavors with a big grin on our faces.

I loved how fun, tasty, and romantic it was to slow down and savor like this. At the end of each mindfulness eating practice, we were always shocked by how little we needed to feel completely full.

Just as Thich Nhat Hanh predicted, we found that we could eat less and feel more nourished, more satiated than ever before. We could afford to buy less and buy organic. I became a huge fan of mindfulness eating practice - so much fun, so delicious, and so economical!

It would be years later in clinical practice that my patients taught me about the deeper therapeutic benefits of mindfulness eating practice.

MINDFULNESS EATING PRACTICE CAN HEAL

My patient (let's call her "Jenny") was struggling with a long history of severe digestive issues. She had a diagnosis of celiac disease, irritable bowel syndrome (IBS), and multiple other chronic inflammatory conditions.

It was difficult for Jenny to digest anything beyond simple miso soup and a little white rice. After much experimentation, she found a special hypoallergenic nutritional shake that helped her to get the fundamental nutrients she needed. Occasionally she would venture slightly outside of her strict regimen (with carefully chosen organic gluten-free allergen-free meals), but she always experienced severe digestive pains.

Despite all this, Jenny had a wonderful attitude on life and remained optimistic about her ongoing healing.

One day, she came to an appointment bursting with joy, eager to share a huge breakthrough!

That weekend, she went to a workshop on mindfulness eating practice at a meditation retreat center. She discovered she was able to eat a variety of foods without any digestive pain!

She experienced this new kind of eating - slowing down, savoring and chewing every bite until it was liquefied. She discovered that, by eating in this state of peace and meditation, chewing slowly, the food is half-digested in the mouth already. So the stomach and intestines had much less work to do. The practice seemed to have shifted her mind-body into a deeply relaxed "parasympathetic" mode, where optimal digestion could occur.

She was shocked and surprised by how many different types of food she could eat without any digestive pains (as was I!).

From that day on, Jenny began to expand her culinary choices little by little, which opened up a whole new world of possibilities.

For decades, her condition had prevented her from participating fully in many social events that surrounded food. Now with the support of mindful eating, she was free to enjoy many new flavors and experiences of life. What a wonderful freedom!

Jenny's case inspired me to take the practice of mindfulness eating much more seriously as a healing tool.

Over the past 20 years, studies have shown that mindful eating can help us:

- reduce overeating and binge eating,
- optimize body weight and reduce BMI,
- decrease anxious thoughts about food, and cope with chronic eating problems such as anorexia and bulimia, and
- improve the symptoms of type 2 diabetes.[63]

Mindful eating can be a deep practice with healing gifts that are unimaginable until we experience it for ourselves. Perhaps that's why it is everyone's favorite experience on the SuperWellness journey.

Participants with a history of digestive issues often report noticeable improvements in their symptoms by slowing down to savor and chew mindfully. Nearly everybody who shares the mindfulness eating practice with us reports far greater enjoyment of their food, more satiation, less food coma, better post-meal energy, and eating less without any calorie counting.

As we slow down our eating, we give the body time to communicate. The stomach has a chance to signal to the brain that it's full and satiated. Our taste buds can tell us what the body truly wants/needs vs. what it doesn't need. When we take time to fully taste our foods, we discover a lot about ourselves.

Plus, the flavors can be delicious beyond imagination.

It's a wonderful experience. Give it a try… today!

SUPERWELLNESS LAB - MINDFULNESS EATING PRACTICE

Join us for a delicious Mindful Eating experience in your book bonuses. Find out why everybody loves it so much.

To prepare for your Mindful Eating:

- gather a small bowl or plate of food,

- get a blindfold (optional but highly recommended),

- wear a bib or napkins (also optional but highly recommended!),

- have your journal ready to jot down your wisdom and insights afterwards, then

- go to www.SuperWellness.com/BookBonuses and play the Mindfulness Eating practice video in your Chapter 6 book bonuses.

Make it extra fun by inviting a friend or family member to share this experience with you. Enjoy!

When you're complete, please share what you experienced with our online community. We look forward to hearing from you!

THE MAGIC OF "INTERMITTENT FASTING"

Our discussion of **Lightening Up** would not be complete without introducing the enormous healing benefits of "Intermittent Fasting." In recent years, Intermittent Fasting (IF) has gained a lot of attention, and it's for very good reason.

Proponents of Intermittent Fasting point out that:

- Human beings have been fasting for thousands of years (both by choice and out of necessity).

- It's only in recent modern times that we habitually eat 3+ meals a day and rarely fast.

- Animals (humans included) will instinctively fast when they are sick.

- All the major religions, including Christianity, Islam, Buddhism, Jainism, Hinduism, advise fasting as part of a spiritual practice.

- The latest scientific literature is demonstrating undeniable evidence of its healing and longevity benefits (details below).

(Warning: Please consult your doctor or professional healthcare providers before trying Intermittent Fasting or embarking on any major changes in your regimen. There are some conditions where fasting is not recommended. Do not engage in prolonged fasting without medical supervision.)

WHAT IS INTERMITTENT FASTING?

"Dr. Edith, I know what 'fasting' means, but what is 'Intermittent Fasting' exactly?"

The term **"Intermittent Fasting"** refers to any eating pattern in which we intentionally cycle between periods of eating and fasting. There are several popular patterns of Intermittent Fasting, with somewhat funny names like "16/8", "Eat-stop-eat", or "5:2."

- **"16/8"**: The easiest of all the Intermittent Fasting patterns is to eat only within an 8 hour window each day. Most of us already "fast" every day while we sleep. (Breakfast is literally the "breaking of fast.") So many people find it easy to extend that window of fasting longer and only eat between, say, 12noon to 8pm. This means fasting for 16 hours and eating only within an 8 hour period. This is known as the **"16/8"** method (also referred to as **"time-restricted eating"**).

- **"Eat-stop-eat"**: Another popular rhythm is to eat normally 6 days a week, and fast 1 day a week, drinking water, tea, or broths only. (E.g. don't eat anything from dinner one evening to dinner the next evening, so fasting for 24 hours once a week.) Some people call this the **"Eat-stop-eat"** or the **"6:1"** method.

- **"5:2"**: The **"5:2"** method has also become popular, where participants eat freely 5 days a week, and limit their caloric intake 2 days of the week to a very minimal 500-600 calories a day.

Regardless of the type of fasting pattern, the scientific evidence is undeniable that Intermittent Fasting can yield powerful longevity and healing benefits.

Intermittent Fasting can:

- improve cellular repair and tissue regeneration,
- balance cholesterol/lipid profile,
- reduce cardiovascular risk factors,
- decrease overall levels of inflammation, [64]
- assist in weight loss and healthy metabolism.[65] [66] [67]
- optimize blood sugar and insulin levels,
- increase human growth hormone levels, [68] [69]
- reduce the risk of many of our modern diseases, including type 2 diabetes, Alzheimer's, cancer, and others [70] [71]
- offer powerful anti-aging and longevity benefits [72]

There's a wonderful BBC documentary called "Eat, Fast, Live Longer" that I encourage you to seek out on the web. It's a fun and entertaining deep dive into this topic of Intermittent Fasting.

"Dr. Edith, the benefits of Intermittent Fasting sound amazing! But fasting requires so much willpower and discipline. I thought you said that willpower was not a long-term solution.

How can Intermittent Fasting be sustainable?"

I'm so glad you asked! You're right. Relying on willpower is not sustainable. Plus, I promised you that SuperWellness is all about tools that are fun, free, and require <u>zero deprivation</u>. So on the surface, Intermittent Fasting doesn't seem to fit with our SuperWellness philosophy.

Here's my breakthrough after years of experimentation...

INTERMITTENT FASTING CAN BE A NATURAL "SIDE-EFFECT" OF FEELING NOURISHED!

In 2009 and 2010, I first learned about the health benefits of Intermittent Fasting and experimented with fasting on water, teas, or broths one day each week. I would fast every Saturday and noticed incredible energy and mental clarity for two or three days afterwards. By fasting on Saturdays, it gave my system a weekly reboot. I naturally ate slower and more mindfully on Sundays, Mondays and Tuesday. So you can say the benefits extended into half the week. It was wonderful.

The problem was, this one day of fasting always required great willpower. It didn't feel sustainable. Gradually, I "fell off the bandwagon."

Then in 2012, I decided to deepen many of the practices that you've experienced so far in Chapters 3, 4, and 5. Rather than focusing on these tools one at a time, I experimented with "stacking" them all together and was shocked to see their synergistic effects, with <u>massive</u> improvements in my mood, energy, productivity, and clarity!

When I integrated ALL the non-food practices we've explored thus far (breathing, Qigong, gratitude, sleeping in darkness, optimal sunshine, time in nature, drinking fresh clean spring water, etc.), **I noticed my hungers diminished dramatically.** I continued to stay fit and strong, running regularly and riding my bicycle long distances, burning lots of calories. Whenever I ate, I practiced listening to my body and followed my personal F.A.N. diet.

By feeding myself in these fun and loving ways, I found myself eating less and feeling much more satiated. Day after day, month after month.

I was surprised to find that various rhythms of "Intermittent Fasting" happened naturally, without any effort. Zero deprivation!

It's as if all the health-promoting lifestyle practices shifted my physiology to a new state, like a big Operating System upgrade. My body felt like a new "hybrid-vehicle" that was tapping into energy from both food and non-food sources.

The "fuel-economy" on my new body-vehicle was unbelievable!

Then as you know, in 2013 I went to Thailand and experienced the incredible gift of the Dark Room Retreat, where we spent nine days and nine nights in deep meditation and complete darkness. While on the retreat, the fasting happened naturally and effortlessly again. It never felt like a fast, but more like a "feast!"

This was my big ah-ha moment. It's possible to **receive all the health benefits of "Intermittent Fasting" without any of the sacrifice or deprivation!** When we nourish ourselves with all the non-food lifestyle practices, there's no need for so much willpower.

"Intermittent Fasting" can be a natural byproduct of nourishing ourselves in those delicious non-food ways.

IS THE HUMAN BODY REALLY A HYBRID VEHICLE?

These fascinating experiences broke all the conventional rules about nutrition that I had been taught, especially the "calories-in calories-out" model. It made me realize that **we need an entirely new model of health that puts food and nutrition back within the context of our overall lifestyle, not as a simple standalone.**

Through direct personal experience, and sharing with thousands of patients and SuperWellness students over these years, it's become clear that our food and caloric needs are tied to many other lifestyle factors. Whether we are stressed or relaxed, whether we're receiving natural sunshine, darkness, breathing, etc., can influence our nutritional needs in profound ways.

Perhaps you've experienced this too?

When I survey my patients and students, everybody nods in agreement. We've all experienced increased hunger and food cravings when we're stressed out or sleep deprived. Many of us have seen dramatic decrease in food cravings when we're relaxed, breathing, and meditating on a Yoga retreat.

With the 24 x 7 chronic stress of our society, what our textbooks consider "normal" is likely far from optimal. Don't you agree?

If it's normal to be stressed out, sick, inflamed, tired, and obese, I prefer not to be so "normal!" What about you?

So the question is: **how might our relationship with food be different if we live in a 24 x 7 state of gratitude, instead of 24 x 7 state of stress?** How might our nutrition and calorie needs change when we're sleeping plenty, getting natural sunshine, breathing more, spending time in nature, optimizing our "EZ Water", etc.?

I believe the answer is - science doesn't know. That's why I am such a fan of Wim Hof. We need many more scientific studies with groups of humans that are trained to tap into this optimal state of well-being.

We need to define a new "normal."

As I traveled around the world, studying with different teachers, and meeting practitioners of various breathwork and yogic practices, I learned that these unusual experiences are actually quite common. Amongst people who cultivate advanced yogic, qigong, or alchemical practices, there can be a variety of interesting physiological experiences that are still poorly understood by our current science.

(Aside: one such strange and highly controversial phenomenon is "Breatharianism." Breatharians claim to be able to live purely on energy, breath, "Qi", or "Prana", requiring little food. Warning: Do not stop eating or engage in prolonged fasting without proper medical supervision! I spent years exploring this fascinating phenomenon of Breatharianism, which may interest some readers, but not others. For those interested, download my special report in your book bonuses.)

Controversies aside, to me there's absolutely nothing controversial about being open to possibilities as we cultivate our state of well-being with greater awareness and loving kindness. Many of us are breaking the old rules like: *"you must eat three meals every day,"* or *"breakfast is the most important meal,"* etc. We are giving our bodies what it needs, not too much, not too little, and at the frequency that feels right for our unique lives. In doing so, many of us are discovering **a new normal**.

Instead of chronic stress, anxiety, fatigue, and obesity being society's norm, let us cultivate a new normal, where health, joy, peace, and fulfillment is our natural state.

Let's make "chronic health" the new normal!

A NEW APPROACH TO JUICE CLEANSING

When it comes to "Lightening up," many of us have tried juicing to cleanse and detoxify. Have you done a juice cleanse before?

Juicing is a popular practice in health and wellness communities. The benefits are wonderful. Most people juice in order to cleanse and detox the body, heal faster, and promote weight loss… But wait, there's more.

In SuperWellness, we've discovered that juicing (and brothing) offers gifts and opportunities far beyond basic cleansing, detox, and weight loss.

- Juicing gives the intestines a break from decades of heavy duty solids. The "bowel rest" is a wonderful opportunity for the digestive tract to heal.

- Juicing can flood the body with easy-to-digest nutrients, giving us a feeling of lightness on all levels.

- When less energy is needed to digest food, more resources can be diverted to healing the body, allowing deeper tissue repair to take place.

- According to Professor Gerald Pollack, plant juices are full of EZ Water, which may directly increase the EZ Water within our body, giving our cells and molecules the necessary electricity to support optimal physiological functions.

- Juicing (and brothing) is a wonderful opportunity to reboot our habits and then return to eating with more mindful awareness.

- Being on a liquid-only diet can save a lot of time, especially if you have a juice shop that prepares/delivers your juice for you.

- Juicing can enhance our mental clarity, allowing us to be more present, more effective and productive in our lives.

- Many people report enhanced sensitivity in their taste and smell after juicing. This increase in awareness can be a useful guide for the body to communicate what foods it prefers or doesn't prefer. This helps us fine-tune our F.A.N. diet, allowing the body to become our best nutritionist!

- Participants often report increased intuitive abilities, when the senses are not dulled by heavy solids.

- Juicing is also a great opportunity for an elimination diet (helping us to identify possible allergens and irritants). Afterwards we can gradually reintroduce food ingredients one-at-a-time to gain greater clarity about our health.

- There's a new spaciousness in our body without heavy solids in the stomach. So the diaphragm is more free to <u>Breathe</u>! In this state, we may experience dramatic breakthroughs in our Breathing and Yoga practices.

Many SuperWellness participants tell us they had tried juice fasting before but were unable to complete the programs successfully. They tell us that juicing the SuperWellness way offers a far deeper, juicier (pun!) and more fulfilling experience than just "detox and lose weight."

In SuperWellness, our intention for juicing is to "lighten up" and experience greater inner awareness, so that we can become the best of ourselves on all levels - body, mind, emotions, and spirit.

So before you plan your next juice cleanse, visit your Chapter 6 book bonuses, which include detailed instructions on how to get the most out of your juicing/liquid days. This guide goes far beyond the conventional understanding of cleansing and weight loss.

Learn how to maximize the benefits of your juicing, the SuperWellness way! Visit: <u>www.SuperWellness.com/BookBonuses/</u>

WHEN WE LIGHTEN UP, WE *FEEL* MORE

Have you ever noticed that when we feel stressed out, sad, or emotional, we tend to gravitate towards comfort foods? Sometimes when we don't want to feel something, we might eat in order to dull our senses. Maybe we eat a big tub of ice cream, a bag of potato chips, or a jar of cookies? I know I've certainly been there.

Sometimes we use food to dampen our feelings, especially when the emotions seem too overwhelming.

When we start to "Lighten Up" our foods, the opposite happens. We feel more clear, more sharp, more alive. We might experience heightened sensitivity to life. For some of us, the enhanced sensitivity can be uncomfortable at first. But with practice, it can be the greatest gift. Being sensitive is a Superpower!

Nowadays, many people out there are living like zombies, going through the motions of life, numbed out and only half living. So when you come alive and awaken all of your sensitivities, everything feels more clear or intense. This can seem like a strange and different feeling. So please be gentle with yourself. Give yourself a healing environment that supports your beautiful transformation.

As you "lighten up" with mindful eating or a juicing cleanse, I always recommend a simultaneous **Digital/Media Detox**. Be very conscious of the digital media that you consume. Become aware of all the information that you surround yourself with, including the quality of conversations that you keep, even the books that you read. Spend more time in nature and less time in front of screens. Give yourself the silence and stillness to create space away from the constant bombardment of negative media that's so rampant today.

Even if the media we consume is not negative, it can still be noisy and distracting. Many of us are struggling to find inner peace and clarity, because we're pulled into constant noise and distraction. Now more than ever, we need to **turn down the noise on the outside, so that we can find our stillness within.**

If you are reading this book, I know you care deeply about the great issues of our world today. You have a passion for bringing forth creative and innovative solutions. For this reason, it is important to take a rest from the digital world and reconnect with the great source of wisdom within.

So for visionary pioneers like you, I recommend a **7 day Digital/Media Detox** at least once a season (every three months). Whenever you are juicing and cleansing, a simultaneous digital detox is a **must** in my opinion.

SUPERWELLNESS LAB - LIGHTEN UP WITH A DIGITAL DETOX

For our SuperWellness Lab this week, please take a 360° survey of the information that you experience through all your digital devices. Could you lighten it up? What's pulling you into unnecessary distraction? How can you minimize your screen time and remain effective at your work?

In your book bonuses, enjoy a video where we explore the intentions and benefits behind doing a Digital Detox.

Here is your Digital Detox checklist:

- **NEWS:** Who would you be, if you didn't watch the news for the next 7 days? (If not feasible, due to professional responsibilities for example, then what if you limit the news to just 10 minutes of headlines only?)

- **COMPUTER:** Can you turn off all those distracting **notifications**? So it doesn't *ding* at you anytime an email comes into your inbox, etc.?

- **EMAIL:** How might your stress levels and productivity change, if you consolidate your email time? Could you set up an autoresponder that reads something like this:

"Thank you for your email! In an effort to enhance my work productivity this week, I'm limiting my email access hours to 2-4pm daily. Thank you

for your understanding. If this is a truly urgent matter, I can be reached by phone (or secretary/assistant, etc.). Otherwise, I look forward to responding to your email within 24hours."

Wow! What would that be like, to free ourselves from email distractions for most of the day?

- **PHONE:** Does your mobile phone *ring*ding*buzz*bing* all day long? Could you turn the phone OFF for a few hours a day, half the day, all day? Could you simply setup a voice-mail greeting to indicate that you check it only at certain hours? When your phone rings or dings with voice mails, text messages, etc., how does your body feel? Is it a peaceful harmonious feeling, or is it a stressful feeling?

- **TV:** What TV shows could you eliminate, or replace with entertainment that's more harmonious with your natural peaceful state? (Remember the "crowding out" strategy in Chapter 1?)

- **MUSIC/OTHER MEDIA:** Do you listen to music that supports your well-being? Consider Masaru Emoto's water crystal experiments on how music can influence our water molecules.

- **GENERAL:** Become aware of the information you expose yourself to throughout the day - the conversations you keep, the books, magazines, and newspapers you read, etc.

After you take a 360° survey, minimize your digital screen time for the next seven days and notice how you feel. Re-evaluate in one week and return to your digital life with a new mindful awareness. Share your experience with us. Let us know how it goes!

PUTTING YOUR LIFE BACK IN YOUR HANDS AGAIN

Did you know that the average American watches 4-5 hours of TV a day?[73] During my certification training as a high performance coach, we did the math and found that this equates to $2 million dollars' worth of income for the average American, over the course of his/her working years.

When I share this stat with our SuperWellness ninjas-in-training, most peoples' immediate reaction is to say they'd never watch that much TV. But when we take a truthful assessment, many of us realize that we're spending 3, 4, 5 hours of precious time each day on social media like Facebook, Instagram, and Twitter. We are being pulled into constant distraction.

So let's be honest. How much time each day do you spend scrolling through social media feeds and getting distracted online? How many hours per week are you watching Netflix or YouTube videos? Is all this time enhancing your sense of peace and well-being? Or is it distracting you from what truly matters - your self-care, your joy, your service to the world, your kids, your family?

Imagine what we could do with 4-5 extra hours each day. Get fit, strong, and healthy? Learn a new language? Build a side-business so that we have freedom to quit the job we don't love? Cultivate deeper relationships with ourselves and our friends and family?

When we lighten up our food and drinks, and remove ourselves from the chronic distractions of digital media, we get back hours of precious free time each day. We can spend those hours on better self-care and choose activities that are far more meaningful, nourishing, and uplifting. Our quality of life can improve in massive ways.

So join us. **Take the 7-Day Digital Detox Challenge. You deserve a good life!**

AN INTIMATE AFFAIR WITH DORITOS CHIPS

As we complete this chapter, I'd love to share with you a fun and powerful little story about Doritos.

One of the participants in our SuperWellness program had a special love for Doritos chips. Of course, he didn't need anybody to tell him that his junk food habit wasn't so great for his health. He often "tried" not to eat too much. It took tremendous willpower to self-regulate on his Doritos consumption.

Then something interesting happened with his Doritos habit during this 'L' module.

With the social support of the entire class together, we all "Lightened up" with the digital detox and juice cleanse. This meant no Doritos! He was surprised how much he loved the three days of juicing, so much so he decided to extend the juicing a couple more days.

He enjoyed everything about the juicing, <u>except</u> one thing - he was always dreaming of eating Doritos!

My instructions for transitioning to eating solids after the juicing was as follows:

"When you break your juice fast, eat anything you like for your very first solid meal, but take advantage of this special moment to listen deeply to your body through Mindful Eating practice. With the Juicing and Digital Detox, your senses become very clear. Your ability to taste, smell, feel is much more heightened. Take advantage of this Superpower!

*For your first solid meal, gather your favorite food(s). Create the space for a slow, delicious mindful eating practice. Chew every bite 30x, 50x, 100x, and allow your body to tell you what it wants, what it doesn't want. Listen deeply and lovingly to your body. Allow your body to **be your own best nutritionist**. You may be surprised."*

So our friend decided: *"I'm gonna break my fast with a big bag of Doritos chips!"*

He opened a bag of Doritos and sat in a state of gratitude and appreciation. He put a chip in his mouth and began chewing very slowly and mindfully.

He set out to chew it 30x, 50x, tasting deeply into all the subtle flavors of the Doritos.

To his shock and surprise, it tasted <u>absolutely awful</u>!

He said it was like cardboard and chemicals. The taste was so unnatural and so artificial, it was almost unbearable to chew mindfully like this. Then he decided to try eating it <u>mindlessly</u>. He 'snarfed' down a few chips the way most people eat junk food. Now, it was addictively "tasty" again!

He tried chewing it mindfully again, and once again it tasted like cardboards and chemicals. Clearly his body was telling him it didn't want this awful stuff! So after just a few chips of experimenting like this, it was enough. He decided to quit the Doritos and go enjoy more fresh, healthy, and alive foods instead.

Just like that, he stopped eating the Doritos. No willpower needed.

When we slow down and listen deeply within, many healthy choices unfold naturally, without needing so many rigid rules.

What interesting insights will come to you this week when you experience your Mindful Eating and Digital Detox? I'm excited for you to find out!

SUMMARY OF 'L' IS FOR LIGHTENING UP

In this chapter, we explored the powerful benefits of "Lightening Up" with

- Mindfulness Eating Practice,
- Intermittent Fasting,
- Liquids, Juicing, Brothing, and
- Digital Detox.

We discovered why sometimes "slower is faster" and "less is more."

SuperWellness participants routinely tell me that they feel more clear, light, and spacious in their bodies, their minds, and their emotions when they implement the tools in this chapter. The gifts are often unimaginable until we experience them directly for ourselves.

Thank you for your commitment to awakening your SuperWellness! Our journey just keeps getting better and better. In the next chapter, we dive into our most exciting and advanced topic yet - **Mind Mastery.**

Let's review our journey thus far:

- 'H' is for coming Home.
- 'E' is for Environment.
- 'A' is for Agua, 'A' was for *Aaaarmph!*
- 'L' is for Lightening up.

Next up, 'T' is for Thoughts, and 'T' is for Truth. We will learn how to manage our stressful thoughts, master our minds, and go deeply within to discover our inner truth.

CHAPTER 7
'T' is for Thoughts, 'T' is for Truth

"Happiness can't be achieved... If we pursue it, it runs away. If we stop pursuing it and question our minds instead, the source of all stress disappears. Happiness is who we already are, once our minds are clear."

~ Byron Katie, creator of "The Work" ~

THE TREASURE IS HIDDEN WITHIN

Accoording to an old Hindu legend, there once was a time when all human beings were gods. But they abused their divinity. So Brahma, the chief god, decided it was necessary to take it away so it could never be found. But where to hide it?

Brahma called a council of gods to help him decide.

"Let's bury it deep in the earth," said the gods.

"No, that will not do, because humans will dig into the earth and find it," said Brahma.

Then the gods said, *"Let's sink it into the deepest ocean."*

Brahma said, *"No not there. They will learn to dive into the ocean and find it."*

Next the gods suggested, *"Let's take it to the top of the highest mountain and hide it there."*

Brahma said, *"No that won't work either. They will eventually climb every mountain and find it."*

So the gods gave up and said, *"We don't know where to hide it then, because it seems there's no place on earth or in the sea that human beings will not eventually reach."*

Brahma contemplated for a long time, and finally he said, *"Here's what we will do. We will hide their divinity **deep into the center of their own being**, for humans will never think to look for it there."*

All the gods agreed that this was the perfect hiding place, and the deed was done.

Ever since then, the story goes, humans have been going all around the earth, digging, diving, climbing, and exploring, **searching for a treasure that is already within themselves.**

LIVING LIFE FROM THE INSIDE OUT, INSTEAD OF OUTSIDE IN

The Hindu legend is a sobering reminder (or a humorous one, depending on how you look at it!) of how often we look everywhere outside ourselves for answers, when the answers are already within. In doing so, we often make life unnecessarily difficult or complicated for ourselves.

When we listen deeply within, we can discover a simple and direct path to our healing, happiness, and freedom. The funny Doritos story of the last chapter is a perfect example of this! Sometimes the solutions are so simple, we just have to laugh.

Carl Jung once said:

"Who looks outside, dreams. Who looks inside, awakens."

As we practice looking within ourselves for solutions, a deeper clarity and wisdom arises. Our entire experience of life starts to shift. When problems are presented, we are less likely to rush into the "blame-game." Instead, we view life through the eyes of wisdom. We address the deeper root cause levels of problems, not just the superficial "band-aid" solutions.

In my experience, meditation can help us tap into this inner wisdom. Perhaps that's why countless studies now confirm that meditation can boost both IQ and EQ ("emotional intelligence"), creativity, insight, and intuition.[74] [75] [76] For me, these are all aspects of our inner wisdom.

Consider the most serious problems facing our world today - environmental degradation, war, poverty, disease, violence, crime and corruption. When you watch the news, have you noticed how politicians debate endlessly about who's to blame, and what regulatory policies must be put in place to control/punish those who are at fault? When it comes to our actions and solutions, it often feels like we're stuck in emergency "fire-fighting" mode, dealing with one crisis after another. But how often do we pause to look at the deeper sources of these problems?

What are the underlying root issues in our human mind that promote these cycles of greed, anger, lack, hatred, and suffering?

Without healing our minds and hearts at the individual level and as a collective human family, our history will likely continue to repeat itself. As the saying goes, *"hurt people hurt people."* It is only when we stop blaming one another and focus on healing that we have a chance to end these cycles of trauma, war and suffering.

Rumi said: *"Yesterday I was clever, so I wanted to change the world. Today I am wise, so I am changing myself."*

Healing ourselves from the inside out is a deep practice. It takes tremendous courage and personal responsibility. I believe it is the only truly viable long-term solution.

As we go deeply within and heal on all levels - body, mind, emotions, and spirit - we start to see life with fresh new eyes. We engage with the world from the place of wisdom and loving action. Through our example, we inspire others to also live from this state of courage and personal responsibility. This is how we can change the world together.

"That's why SuperWellness is more than just a formula for health. It's really a new state of being for humanity. Healing ourselves is the most effective way to change the world."

So with the deepest respect, I bow to your mastery! Thank you for becoming your own best healer. Thank you for doing your inner work. Our world needs it now more than ever.

ALIGNING WITH OUR INNER TRUTH

At our clinic, patients come in for the treatment of a broad range of health conditions, such as chronic aches and pains, digestive issues, hormonal imbalances, insomnia, hypertension, and immune complaints. While each case is unique, I've noticed an important pattern.

Nearly all patients who come in for chronic health ailments also express a deep dissatisfaction with a certain aspect of their lives. When they choose to listen to that inner voice and realign their lives, very often their healing is accelerated in dramatic ways.

Holistic healing modalities like acupuncture, sound healing, bodywork therapies, etc. help us to shift into a state of peace and tranquility. This state is a wonderful and much needed relief from the stresses of our world today. But in my experience, the true healing results are always determined by the patient himself/herself.

Will the patient choose to maintain this state of tranquility and alignment in daily life? Or will they go right back into living an out-of-balance, stressful, or unfulfilling life as soon as they walk out the door?

Over the course of my career, I've worked with thousands of patients with chronic or complex health issues. I've noticed that patients **who heal the quickest tend to be those who take advantage of the pain or illnesses as opportunities to listen deeply within.** For example, during acupuncture, patients drift into a deep and meditative state, from which sudden insights or wisdom may arise effortlessly. When we complete the session, many patients report a new level of clarity about how to realign certain aspects of their lives.

Not every patient acts on this clarity or insight. It takes courage to change. Time and time again, I've noticed that the patients who act on these insights often see faster healing results.

One such patient was "Christina" who came to my clinic because of a debilitating painful spasm in her neck. She woke up one morning in severe pain, unable to move her neck, and assumed she had "slept on it wrong." During our appointment, I evaluated her neck carefully and saw all the musculoskeletal issues that needed to be addressed.

Since Orthopedics and Sports Medicine was my original specialty (I teach professional certification courses in this specialty), I went to work on Christina's neck right away, with great confidence.

After our first session of acupuncture and manual therapy, she was 90% better! Christina and I were thrilled! But unfortunately, the effects didn't last. Just a few days later, the pain returned and gradually worsened throughout the work week. At her second session, again she was 90% better after the treatment. But again the pain returned three or four days later. It became clear that my treatment was only addressing the symptom and not the root cause.

So during our third appointment, instead of going to work on her neck, Christina and I discussed more deeply about the history and onset of this injury. This time, as she recounted the events leading up to her pain, she realized it was after a very stressful conversation with her manager at work. Christina didn't feel comfortable speaking her truth, and it left her very upset. That night she slept poorly and woke up with the spasm in the neck the next morning. She never found the courage to speak up and bring the situation back to resolution.

In speaking about it, she realized it was still causing a great deal of stress. So I invited Christina to consider the possibility that this uneasy and stressful situation at work may be directly impacting her neck pain.

Upon reflection, Christina agreed that the stress with her manager was at least a contributing factor, if not the cause. So that week, she mustered up the courage to speak honestly and openly with her manager. They had a wonderful meeting and brought the situation to a harmonious resolution.

At our next appointment, Christina was beaming with joy about how well the meeting went. She told me that the neck pain was more than **50% better** immediately after the meeting! In this session, our acupuncture and manual therapy gave us by far the fastest results to date. We easily returned the neck to a 100% pain free state, with full range of motion. According to Christina, it has remained healthy and pain free ever since.

That was two years ago. Recently, Christina came in for a general wellness appointment and reminded me of this interesting story, and how grateful she feels to have learned an important life lesson about our mind-body connection.

She now sees listening to her body as not just a key to her health, but a great source of wisdom and inner guidance.

Perhaps you've also had a similar experience in your past? A situation where your body became sick or injured, and it caused you to listen more deeply within and align with your inner truth?

I applaud Christina - and you! This kind of inner awareness is unusual in our world! Please pat yourself on the back. I believe that learning to listen deeply and lovingly to our body is one of the most important factors on any healing journey.

"But Dr. Edith, wouldn't it be better if we could listen to the body's guidance before the onset of pain, illness, or injury?"

Yes. Wow! Sounds like you're ready for the advanced ninja tools!

You're going to LOVE this entire chapter.

YOUR BODY IS COMMUNICATING; ARE YOU LISTENING?

Our human body is an incredibly elegant bio-computer, always responding to our mind and emotions, and always sensing into each situation. When we learn how to listen to the body, we can tap into our intuition and better see/sense/feel if a situation is harmonious and true for us, or if it is inharmonious and false. It's like a lie-detector test.

Surely we've all had the experience of "feeling into" situations. E.g.: *"I have a gut feeling about this situation,"* or *"I have a very good feeling about it!"* or *"something feels a little off about this."* These feelings are our body's way of telling us if a situation is harmonious and aligned with our truth, or inharmonious and out-of-alignment.

Learning to listen to these subtle sensations is a practical skill that can serve us in many situations. It's a wonderful Superpower!

"Dr. Edith, this seems like the most important skill ever, to learn how to listen to our body. **Why did you wait until now to tell us about this?"**

I'm so glad you asked! I waited for a very important reason. It's because our feeling sense can be muddled by so many factors in our lifestyle that, for most people, it's too difficult to tap into this kind of inner awareness.

For example, we often talk about *"listening to our gut feeling."* But imagine if you just ate a bad enchilada, and it caused stomach cramps. How could you listen to your "gut feeling" in that state? When you encounter a situation and had a bad "gut feeling"... is it the situation? Or is it the bad enchilada? It's too difficult to know!

Our journey of H.E.A.L. was carefully designed to create the ideal foundation, so that we can get the most out of listening to the body for intuitive guidance. After we learn to optimize our lifestyle - with breathing, meditation, gratitude, optimizing our environment, purifying our food and drinks and lightening up on all levels - now we have far greater awareness and receptivity to our inner guidance.

As we become more healthy, grounded, and clear, our senses are more heightened. It becomes far easier to cultivate our inner awareness and intuitive abilities.

So please take a moment and celebrate your H.E.A.L.-ing journey. Now we can get the most out of these next-level ninja tools!

The first tool I'd like to share with you is a body awareness exercise called the "**Truth vs. Falsehood Body Test.**" I've learned different variations of this practice from many teachers over the years, which helped me to appreciate how important and useful this kind of inner awareness can be.

It's an indispensable tool for all SuperWellness heroes.

SUPERWELLNESS LAB - THE TRUTH VS. FALSEHOOD BODY TEST

In this exercise, you'll learn how to feel more deeply into the sensations of the body, and utilize these sensations as information and guidance. Keep an open mind. You may be surprised how much your body communicates with you!

1) Begin by stating something <u>simple and true</u>, like:
   "My name is (your name), and I'm a kind and loving human being."
   Or *"My name is (your name), and I am here."*

2) Say this simple statement a few times out loud and also silently in your mind. As you say it, scan your body and notice how your body feels? How is your breathing, your heart-rate, your skin temperature, your sense of relaxation vs. tension in the body?

3) Now for contrast, say something that is obviously <u>not true</u>, like: *"My name is John Doe, and I'm a (fill in something totally untrue)."* E.g.: *"My name is John Doe and I'm a criminal."* (or say *"I'm a man"* if you're a woman, and say *"I'm a woman"* if you're a man. Choose any statement that is <u>not true</u> for you.)

As you speak the "lie" both out loud and silently in your mind, notice how this false statement feels in your body? How is your breathing, your heart-rate, your skin temperature, your sense of relaxation vs. tension?

4) Now return to the first <u>true</u> statement again. Speak it a few times until you return to your natural harmonious state.

5) Once you familiarize yourself with these contrasting sensations, you have a reference point for how your body feels when something is truthful and harmonious, vs. something that is false and inharmonious. Perhaps your breathing becomes shallow and you feel tense with "heebie-jeebies" when the statement is false? On the other hand, with the true statement perhaps you feel more calm, relaxed, and centered?

Now that you're aware of how your body speaks to you, you can take advantage of this tool in many day-to-day life situations, almost like a lie detector test.

For example, let's say you're invited to two parties on the same night, and they both sound good. Let your body help you break the tie! You can say out loud: "I want to go to Party A" or "I want to go to Party B." Allow your body to show you which one feels more harmonious and true for you.

(Note: for big important life choices like moving to a new city, getting married, changing careers, etc., I recommend a deeper meditative tool that you will learn in the next chapter.)

This intuitive body feeling can be useful to help break a tie when logic says both choices are equal.

To support you in practicing this "Truth vs. Falsehood Body Test", we created a guided video for you. Visit:

www.SuperWellness.com/BookBonuses/ and discover how to use this wonderful tool to cultivate a new relationship with your body as a guide.

THE POWER OF TRUTH

This "Truth vs. Falsehood Body Test" inspires many SuperWellness heroes to deepen their appreciation of the mind-body connection. We cultivate an inner awareness that is far more subtle and advanced than is normally studied in the conventional science of mind-body medicine. The insights are often profound and life-changing.

How many times a day do we speak our truth? How many times a day do we hold back, or say something that is not exactly honest, perhaps due to social pressures?

When we speak our truth (even though sometimes this takes enormous courage), our body will tell us that it feels at peace. There is a feeling of calm confidence that washes over our body when we stand in our truth and act in integrity.

When we do not speak our truth, or when we live out-of-alignment with our integrity, the body will respond with a certain level of stress and physical tension.

By practicing our "Truth vs. Falsehood Body Test," we learn to listen in this way. We begin to understand why truthful and authentic living may be a critical component of long-term health, whereas stressful thoughts or inharmonious situations can create chronic tension and energy blockage to the body.

IS YOUR QI FLOWING?

Dr. John Sarno, MD (1923-2017) was a legendary pioneer in the field of mind-body medicine who wrote several groundbreaking books. He coined the term **"Tension Myositis Syndrome" (TMS)** to describe how our chronic mental and emotional tension can create physical tension, which causes physical tissues to suffer from chronic low-grade oxygen deprivation. This tension and blockage sets the stage for physical pain, illness, functional limitations, even disability.

In Traditional Chinese Medicine, there's no term for "stress" in the original medical literature. The term is "**Qi Stagnation**" or "Energy

Stagnation." When we encounter mental or emotional stress, our mind becomes tense, and our breathing becomes shallow. This naturally leads to physical tension and chronic low-grade oxygen deprivation. Chinese Medicine goes further by explaining that Qi is the energy that guides our blood circulation. So when the Qi is stagnant, the blood circulation also becomes stagnant. With this chronic low-grade blockage in our circulation, our tissues do not receive the nutrition that they need, and metabolic waste cannot be removed efficiently. This chronic blockage leads to tissue malnutrition, toxicity, inflammation, and pain. It sets the stage for chronic disease to take hold.

The truth is, we've all heard about how stress can impact our health. But integrating these ideas into our lives is an entirely different story.

As Wim Hof likes to say - *"Feeling is understanding."* When we experience tools like "The Truth vs. Falsehood Body Test", we start to really understand how living a life that is out of harmony with our inner truth can be a significant risk factor for pain, illness, or disease. Living a life that's truthful, joyful, and harmonious can be the key to our health and healing.

It's a smart and practical way to live, and there's nothing *"woo-woo"* about that.

THE 9 KEY FACTORS OF RADICAL REMISSIONS

Have you ever heard of a book called *"Radical Remission"* by **Dr. Kelly Turner**? If you haven't yet, I highly recommend looking up her work. It's powerful and "radical" stuff! (Visit www.RadicalRemission.com .)

Dr. Turner is a PhD researcher and psychotherapist who specializes in integrative oncology. She wanted to know how people who experienced complete "remission" from cancer were able to beat the odds. So she meticulously researched over a thousand cases of "Radical Remission" i.e. people who defied the odds of a serious or terminal cancer diagnosis and completely reversed their disease.

The results were revolutionary.

When Dr. Turner analyzed the data, she discovered that there were 75 total factors that influenced the healing of these 1000+ people's healing journey. Not all 75 factors were present in every case, but nearly all the cases had **9 key factors** in common!

What were these 9 factors?

- **taking control of your health,**
- radically changing your diet,
- **following your intuition,**
- taking herbs and supplements,
- **releasing suppressed emotions,**
- **increasing positive emotions,**
- **embracing social support,**
- **deepening your spiritual connection, and**
- **having a strong reason for living.**[77] [78]

Wow. Isn't it fascinating that only two of these are physical/nutritional, whereas seven of the nine are mental, emotional, and spiritual?

For me, Dr. Turner's research is undeniable evidence that our health goes far beyond just the workings of the physical body "machinery." For true healing to occur, we must understand the power of our mind. The mind can be a great source of suffering and dis-ease, but it can also be a great source of joy, health, and healing.

YOUR MIND IS POWERFUL - USE WISELY

The "Placebo Effect" is a classic example of the power of our minds.

In drug trials and medical research, "placebo" is a substance or treatment that is thought to have no active therapeutic effect. It's made to resemble the active medication or therapy, so that it can serve as a control. This prevents the recipient (and others) from knowing whether a treatment is active or inactive, because expectations are known to influence the results.

"Placebo Effect" is the beneficial effect produced by a placebo (i.e. "fake" or "inert") treatment, that is due to the patient's belief or expectations, rather than due to the active treatment itself.

As you can imagine, in drug trials, pharmaceutical companies might like to see the placebo control group experience minimal effects, compared to the group that received the active drug, indicating a highly efficacious drug. But the trouble is, this is never true. The placebo often accounts for a large portion of the therapeutic results.

A 2014 study by Harvard Professor Ted Kapchuk and his colleagues, published in Science Translational Medicine, found that **placebo effect may be equal to the pharmacological effect** in its impact on the recipient's therapeutic result. In other words, it's 50-50 placebo.

In this intricately designed study, participants who suffered from migraine headaches were either given a placebo pill or a migraine drug called Maxalt. But the study didn't just compare Maxalt with placebo, it analyzed how labeling the drug differently could change the therapeutic effects.

The placebo pills were given to participants with three possible labels: 1) "placebo", or 2) "Maxalt or placebo", or 3) "Maxalt." What were the results? The therapeutic effects increased progressively with these labels.

The actual Maxalt pills were also labeled as 1) "placebo", or 2) "Maxalt or placebo", or 3) "Maxalt." Once again, they found that the therapeutic effects increased progressively depending on the label as well.

After analyzing the data, researchers discovered that the **placebo effect accounted for 50% of the drug's therapeutic effects**. And the **labeling significantly influenced the results**.[79]

As a general rule, the placebo effect can vary widely from 18% to 80% in different drug trials.[80] It's an ever present effect, which points to just how powerful our minds can be. This is very good news if we can learn to wield this power!

"Well, Dr. Edith, that's interesting, but pain level is so subjective. It's probably more susceptible to psychological influence than other conditions, right? Show me some more hard science."

Ok. hang on tight - this one will knock your socks off!

Did you know? In clinical trials of Rogaine, the hair re-growth product, individuals in the placebo group grew hair?

Here's an excerpt from a study with 2000+ subjects. Not only did participants in the placebo group stop losing hair, they even regrew a small amount of hair! Check this out:

> "Compared to mean baseline counts of 103-106/cm2, at the end of 32 weeks treatment mean increases in non-vellus hair counts were 39/cm2 in subjects who received 5% TMS (N=163), 30/cm2 in subjects who received 2% TMS (N=79), and **5/cm2 in subjects who received placebo (N=79)**. In the other study, compared to mean baseline counts of 144-152 /cm2, at the end of 48 weeks treatment mean increases in non-vellus hair counts were 19/cm2 in subjects who received 5% TMS (N=137), 13/cm2 in subjects who received 2% TMS (N=139), and **4/cm2 in subjects who received placebo (N=70)**".[81]

Dr. Lissa Rankin, MD author of a bestselling book called *"Mind Over Medicine"* shares that the placebo effect has been found to dilate bronchial tubes, heal ulcers, make warts disappear, lower blood pressure, and many other measurable physiological effects.[82]

THE "NOCEBO" EFFECT - PLACEBO'S SHADOWY TWIN

Placebo also has a shadowy twin called the **"Nocebo"** effect, i.e. a negative placebo effect. Countless studies have documented the possibility of placebo recipients experiencing very real negative side-effects of a drug, even though they were given nothing but an inactive placebo. For example, in chemotherapy trials, participants who were given a simple saline bag experienced nausea, vomiting, even hair loss! [83]

For this reason, pioneers in the field of mind-body medicine now caution patients and doctors about this negative "power of suggestion" in the medical setting.

The challenge is that our doctors were trained to warn patients of all the "worse-case scenario" risks, dangers, and side-effects. Doctors have patient's best interest at heart and are required by law to adhere to strict professional liability. The process of "informed consent" requires that doctors warn patients of potential risks and worse-case scenarios.

But do our doctors receive sufficient training on how to offer this delicate guidance, while minimizing the power of negative suggestion or "nocebo" effect?

What happens within a patient's mind when the doctor tells them a bad prognosis or "it's incurable", etc.?

The truth is, as we explored in Chapter 2 of this book, many of our modern chronic health conditions are considered "cause unknown" or "mysterious" or "incurable" by conventional medicine today. When we view the situation from a pure conventional medicine perspective, the prognosis may seem very poor, or even hopeless, at first glance. Yet it's not uncommon to see patients with these types of conditions experience dramatic improvements, recovery, or even complete remission, when they decide to take personal control and explore alternative options.

At the **Institute of Noetic Sciences** in Petaluma, California, there is a *"Spontaneous Remission Bibliography Project"* with an enormous collection of data on spontaneous remissions, featuring 3500 scientific articles from 800 countries in 20 languages.[84] It seems there are documented cases of remission from nearly every type of so-called "incurable" or "mysterious" condition.

Perhaps you have "beaten the odds" yourself? Or know a loved one who did? Please share your inspiring story with our SuperWellness community! (www.SuperWellness.com) We love to hear about your journey.

"BELIEVE THE DIAGNOSIS, BUT DON'T BELIEVE THE PROGNOSIS." – DEEPAK CHOPRA

Have you ever received a serious or concerning diagnosis from a doctor?

The 2017 documentary "HEAL" explores the powerful impact that our minds can have on our healing. In the film, **Dr. Deepak Chopra** offers an empowering message:

*"If you have a chronic illness, **believe the <u>diagnosis</u>, but don't believe the <u>prognosis</u>."***

Wise words, don't you agree?

There's so much more to explore about how to respond to a doctor's <u>diagnosis</u>, while questioning the <u>prognosis</u>. If you haven't seen HEAL yet, it's a must see!

The documentary features many of my favorite experts, healers, researchers, and pioneers in the field of holistic health and mind-body medicine, including **Dr. Joe Dispenza** (author of *"You Are The Placebo"*), **Bruce Lipton** (author of *"Biology of Belief"* and pioneer in epigenetics), **Gregg Braden** (author of "The *Divine Matrix"*, *"The Spontaneous Healing of Belief"*, and *"Human by Design"*), **Dr. Kelly Turner** (*"Radical Remission"*), **Anthony William** (*"Medical Medium"*), **Dr. Joan Borysenko, Marianne Williamson, Dr. Michael Bernard Beckwith, Dr. Kelly Brogan**, and more! It is a truly star-studded cast. The cinematography, the story telling, the music - I loved everything about it and feel confident you will too!

Visit <u>www.HEALdocumentary.com</u> .

WHAT ARE YOUR FAVORITE STRESS-BUSTING TOOLS?

Now that we understand the profound importance of healing our minds and emotions, and eliminating stress, let me ask you - what are your favorite stress-busting tools?

Many SuperWellness heroes tell us they love their:

- daily breathing or meditation practices,
- gratitude journaling,
- playing with their children or grandchildren,
- acupuncture, massage and bodywork,

- yoga, qigong or taichi,

- music, singing, and dancing,

- sports and movement,

- taking a long bath, and

- spending time in nature.

I love all of these too. What are your favorites?

Do you make it a priority to take care of your stress consistently? What daily habits do you practice to shift yourself out of stress and into the state of peace and tranquility?

Given our new understanding of how critically important this is for our health, I believe it's time for all of us to make this a high priority again.

That's why I recommend every SuperWellness hero block off time on a daily basis for cultivating mental, emotional, and spiritual well-being. Schedule these into your calendar. Make them "non-optional" in your life, on par with brushing your teeth and drinking water!

Your health, your family, your coworkers, and our world depend on you taking beautiful care of yourself on all levels. Thank you for cultivating the very best you!

When it comes to a practical and powerful tool for shifting our energy state out of stress, one of my favorites is called EFT, Emotional Freedom Technique, also known as Tapping.

Now to be honest, when I first came across EFT, I thought it was a little "new-agey" even for me! But when I gave it a try, there was an instant shift in my stress and energy levels, and I quickly became a fan. EFT has become extremely popular in personal development and holistic health circles, and it's for very good reason. Many highly successful leaders, entrepreneurs, and healers swear by it as their go-to stress-busting tool.

So if this is your first time hearing about EFT, I invite you to keep an open mind, try it out, and then decide for yourself.

SUPERWELLNESS LAB – EMOTIONAL FREEDOM TECHNIQUE (EFT)

What is EFT? EFT is a modern form of acupressure that can be helpful for shifting our psychological and emotional energy patterns. It was first introduced by Gary Craig in 1995 and is based on the same energy meridian system used in traditional Chinese acupuncture.

In EFT, special acupuncture/acupressure-points are tapped using the fingers, while the participant speaks positive affirmations. This process is believed to shift the body's bioenergy system and help clear stressful emotions. In my experience, any tool that reduces stress can be a valuable supplement, because returning the mind and body back to a state of balance is the foundation for all healing.

Visit your Chapter 7 book bonuses, where you will find a guided video introducing the EFT "basic recipe." Give it a try and see for yourself! www.SuperWellness.com/BookBonuses/

For readers who are interested in learning more about EFT, or to find professional Official EFT Practitioners, please visit www.emofree.com .

(Note: A reminder that all information in this book is intended for educational purposes only and not meant to diagnose or treat any medical or psychiatric conditions. Please always consult your health/medical practitioners regarding your individual condition, including your use of EFT or any other tools introduced this book.)

We now have access to so many wonderful tools for dealing with our stress, enhancing our well-being, and awakening our highest human potential. What an incredible time to be alive!

In my personal and clinical experience, many tools are highly effective at quickly shifting us out of "fight-or-flight" and into "rest-and-recovery" mode. This is a wonderful gift! But all too often, these results are only short lived. If we walk out of a healing session and go right back to living our old and unhealthy patterns, then the stress-relief is only temporary.

The only long-term solution is to address the root causes of our stress.

We may point to many external factors as the causes of stress in our lives. For example, our job, our spouse, our lack of money, the politicians, our morning commute, or our relationships. But ultimately, if we have the courage to look deeply enough, we discover only **one source of stress**. It's our mind. Our stressful thoughts and beliefs lead to our greatest suffering. When our mind shifts, everything shifts.

After traveling all around the world, studying with masters, teachers, and healers from many different traditions, I've found that they all share this simple teaching:

Everything begins in the mind. Learn to master your mind.

Have you ever noticed how our mind can hang onto stories about the past or the future, creating much of our worries and anxieties? These stressful thoughts limit our perceptions of the grander possibilities of life. They may even cause us to engage with our relationships in unhealthy or distorted ways. If we have the courage to look deeply enough, we start to understand that this is the true source of our suffering.

This is very good news! It means that, once again, we're in charge of our own happiness! It means that when we understand how to work with our minds and heal those stressful thoughts and limiting beliefs, we can experience true freedom from stress.

"Wow. Dr. Edith, that sounds like enlightenment you're talking about! Who doesn't want to be so stress-free, so open, so present and enlightened? But how?"

Of course there are many paths to this kind of inner awakening. I encourage everyone to find the path(s) that work for them.

For me, after decades of exploring countless tools, if I had to choose my #1 favorite one, it would be **The Work of Byron Katie**. It's my favorite practice for working with stressful thoughts and going deeply within to find wisdom, clarity, and truth.

When we learn to find that inner clarity, stress and confusion ends. And we can all tap into this state of freedom, without exception.

THE WORK OF BYRON KATIE

Are you familiar with Byron Katie's "The Work?"

According to Byron Katie's website and the stories she shares in videos and workshops, it all began in 1986 after a life-changing realization. Katie had been deeply depressed, angry, and suicidal for over a decade. One morning in 1986, she says, "enlightenment walked in."

In that moment, she discovered a simple and profound truth:

"When I believed my thoughts, I suffered. But when I didn't believe them, I didn't suffer. And this is true for every human being. Freedom is as simple as that. I found that suffering is optional. I found a joy within me that has never disappeared, not for a single moment. That joy is in everyone, always." (from ByronKatie.com)

"The Work" is Byron Katie's brilliant process of self-inquiry. She says she did not "develop" it, but rather *"The Work woke up within her."*

I am a huge fan of "The Work" because it's a very simple, no-nonsense process of getting still and understanding how our mind works. **Instead of running away from our stressful thoughts, we make friends with our stressful thoughts.** We go deeply within to allow an inner truth and inner wisdom to arise.

Below is a brief introduction to this simple and powerful process of inquiry. For full instructions, please visit TheWork.com; everything you need to begin doing "The Work" is available there - for free!

1) First, write down your stressful thoughts about a specific situation. At TheWork.com, you can find their worksheet called the **"Judge-Your-Neighbor Worksheet"**, with an exact structure for writing down your stressful thoughts and beliefs.

2) Ask yourself **4 simple questions** in a state of stillness and meditation (see TheWork.com for these 4 powerful questions). Allow the insights and answers to surprise you.

3) Do what Byron Katie calls **"The Turnaround"** - i.e. consider the opposite(s) of your original thought and see if it's also true? (Again, see details of how the "Turnaround" works at TheWork.com)

In my experience, this simple process is nothing until we put it into practice in a specific situation that's causing us stress. When we answer the simple questions as genuinely and honestly as we can, incredible discoveries are possible. My experience with The Work is not just an intellectual process as it may seem on the surface, but a very deep meditation and contemplation practice.

From this state of stillness and meditation, we learn to make friends with our fears and anxieties, instead of running away from them.

If you're a Star Wars fan like me, you've likely heard these wise words from Yoda: *"Named must your fear be, before banish it you can."*

Byron Katie goes one step further. Through The Work, we go far beyond naming and accepting our fears. We learn to embrace them, love them, and make friends with them. Our fears, anxieties, and stressful thoughts give us powerful opportunities for learning and growth. When we do this kind of inquiry, our fears are transmuted into pure unconditional love. We may discover that there was nothing to fear after all. Sometimes the most scary and stressful situations turn into the most funny and lovable ones. Fear turns into genuine laughter and humor. We fall madly in love with life again.

In Chapter 2, I shared with you the sudden awakening experience in 2003 that changed my perception of life overnight. From that day on, I became a seeker, reading hundreds of books, and traveling all around the world to study with teachers, healers, and wisdom keepers. Gradually, the puzzle pieces started falling into place. Today, the best treasures are distilled into this book that you're now holding in your hands.

On this journey, every teacher and method offered powerful gifts. But without a doubt, Byron Katie's "The Work" had the greatest and most long-lasting impact in my life. It's a practical tool that cuts right to the chase, turning every problem into an opportunity for growth. It's a trusty friend that has accompanied me through life's greatest ups and downs. Through years of practicing "The Work", I discovered that every moment is a chance to create heaven on earth. This is not just a nice idea, but a practical and much more enjoyable way to live life!

I've introduced "The Work" to thousands of clients and students by now, and nearly everybody tells me it was a "game-changer" in their lives. I invite you to visit www.TheWork.com to learn more.

"Is it true?"
"Who would you be without your story?"

~ Byron Katie ~

SUPERWELLNESS LAB - LEARN ABOUT BYRON KATIE'S "THE WORK"

1) See "The Work" in action! Go online and watch a video called "**Dyslexia and the Idea of Disability**, Part 1 & Part 2." (A web search will turn it up easily.) It's my all-time favorite Byron Katie video. She does "The Work" with a dyslexic man who feels distraught over his reading and writing disabilities. Discover how a stressful situation can turn into one filled with love and gratitude - all by asking 4 simple questions.

2) Go to TheWork.com - everything you need to get started doing The Work is available there for free.

3) To dive deeper, read any of Byron Katie's wonderful books, such as: "Loving What Is", "I Need Your Love, Is That True?", or "A Thousand Names For Joy."

Enjoy! I'm excited to hear what you think.

Note: Besides being a graduate of many of Byron Katie's workshops, I am not affiliated with their organization and receive no compensation (except the joy in my heart) for referring you to her work. Her programs transformed my life in the most beautiful ways, and I hope they will support you on your journey as well!

THE POWERFUL STORY OF ANITA MOORJANI

As we conclude this chapter, I'd love to share with you the incredible story of Anita Moorjani, which radically transformed my understanding of health and healing.

Have you heard of Anita Moorjani?

In 2006, Anita was dying of Stage 4B Lymphoma after a four year battle. Her body was ridden with lemon-sized tumors, and she fell into a deep coma. Her organs were failing, and doctors expected she had only hours to live. She entered into a Near Death Experience (NDE) where she went to "the other realm."

Her book *"Dying To Be Me"* recounts this incredible story of her journey to the other realm, where she realized that "heaven" is not a destination, but rather a state of being. Anita shares beautiful details of the experience, including love-filled encounters with her father, who had died ten years prior, and a best friend who had passed on just three years before.

According to Anita, many aspects of her life became clear in that state of expanded awareness. She realized that her body was a mere reflection of her internal state. She "knew" that if she could bring back this state of love and fearlessness as she returned to her body, she would heal rapidly.

This is exactly what happened. She returned from the coma and recovered at a pace that defied all medical understanding. Her case shocked everybody, doctors and family members alike. Within two days, her organ functions returned. **Within a few weeks, all her cancer was undetectable.** She was released from the hospital within 5 weeks and remains cancer-free today.

Anita's powerful story inspires us to consider that living life from the state of love, instead of fear, could be the biggest difference-maker of all. For example, when we practice our healthy lifestyle tools, is it driven by a **fear of disease**? Or is it driven by our **love** for life? This inner state of being may have the greatest influence of all.

As you reflect on our SuperWellness journey thus far, I hope you agree it's been filled with fun, joy and a palpable love for life! I've come to see that this love and joy is the "secret sauce" to success in any endeavor in life, not just SuperWellness.

Anita's story underscores the idea that our **inner state of being** may be even more important than our external actions. She inspires us to embrace life with pure love, an open mind, and an open heart.

Visit Anita Moorjani's website www.AnitaMoorjani.com to learn more about her inspiring story. Her book *"Dying To Be Me"* is a wonderful and joyful read, which blew my mind in the most beautiful way. Highly recommended.

SUMMARY OF 'T' IS FOR THOUGHT, 'T' IS FOR TRUTH

Wow! You did it. Congratulations on your courage and openness to study these highly advanced tools. Mastering our minds, understanding our stressful thoughts, and going deeply within to find our truth is an advanced lifelong practice.

I honor you for challenging yourself to do this important work.

In this chapter, we burst open an exciting new world of possibilities, tapping into the power of our minds to heal our bodies. We learned how we can work with our stressful 'T'houghts and align with our inner 'T'ruth.

We explored advanced topics like:

- "The Truth vs. Falsehood Body Test",
- Dr. Kelly Turner's Radical Remission research,
- "Tension Myositis Syndrome (TMS)" and "Qi Stagnation",
- The Placebo and Nocebo Effects,
- Dr. Deepak Chopra: *"Believe the diagnosis, don't believe the prognosis"*,
- Prioritizing your stress-reduction practices,
- Emotional Freedom Technique (EFT), aka "Tapping",
- "The Work" of Byron Katie, and
- The inspiring story of Anita Moorjani.

We also gained a deeper understanding of the synergistic relationship between all our SuperWellness tools and topics thus far. Each stage of our H.E.A.L.T.H. journey sets us up perfectly for success with the subsequent stage.

Many SuperWellness participants tell us that they had already tried many of these self-care tools before, in no particular order. But when these tools are "stacked" together in our exact step-by-step sequence, even the highly experienced wellness pro is blown away by the results.

- "H" is for coming Home.
- "E" is for Environment.
- "A" is for Agua and *Aaaarmph!*
- "L" is for Lightening Up.
- "T" is for Thoughts and Truth.

In the next chapter, our final stage of "Part II: The Recalibration" comes full circle back to "H" again. *Home is where the heart is.* This time, **"H" is for Heart**. Everybody speaks about living from the heart, or embracing life with a big open heart. But what does it really mean?

In Chapter 8, we will demystify it all and discovery why "Heart-based living" is our natural, joyful, and loving state.

The research shows that "Heart-based living" is the optimal flow-state in which productivity skyrockets, and inspiration and teamwork is maximized. We radiate healing energy that leads to measurable benefits for our friends, family, and the world around us. So let us take our journey back to the center of our being, back into our heart.

CHAPTER 8

'H' is for Living from the Heart

*"It is only with the Heart that one can see rightly;
What is essential is invisible to the eye."*

~ *Antoine de Saint-Exupery* ~

THE HEART HAS SUPERPOWERS!

In early 2011, I learned the power of "Living from the Heart" through a series of surprising and magical events. I discovered that the heart can "see" far beyond what the rational mind can perceive.

Back then, my clinical practice in San Francisco was operating out of a much smaller office space. The lease was coming to a close. I wanted to expand to a bigger space but was feeling nervous and apprehensive about the change.

To make matters worse, San Francisco officially became the most expensive city in the world. Rental prices were skyrocketing, and availabilities were extremely scarce. For months, I spent all my extra time looking around the city for a new office space within my budget. Month-after-month, no luck. I was running out of time.

Then one day, I was walking near Golden Gate Park and saw a *"for rent"* sign at a mysterious-looking storefront. The store was closed, but I felt a magnetic pull towards it, so I searched online to find it listed on *Craigslist*. Again, the price was far beyond my budget, so I sighed and kept walking.

"Oh well. This isn't the neighborhood I was planning on anyway. Keep looking."

But for days afterwards, I couldn't forget about that *"for rent"* sign near Golden Gate Park. So I called the number and scheduled a viewing just to satisfy my curiosity and see what the inside looked like. It turned out, the current tenant was a professional sound healer and the world's top distributor of Tibetan Singing Bowls. No wonder I was magnetically drawn to the energy of this space!

He shared how he moved all of his retail business to the internet and no longer needed this store. That's why his shop was rarely open, and he made the Craigslist posting in an effort to transition out of his lease early. To be honest, there was absolutely nothing fancy or beautiful about the space. Boring white walls, tons of boxes and shelves. I couldn't see how this space could possibly transform into a holistic wellness clinic without a massive renovation project that went far beyond my budget.

Plus, this wasn't in my ideal neighborhood, and the asking rent price was far too high. So I thanked him for the viewing and left.

That week, I went to Sedona, Arizona for a meditation workshop with a wonderful teacher named Drunvalo Melchizedek.

In this workshop, Drunvalo taught a powerful **Heart Meditation** practice; he called it "going into the sacred space of the heart." There were aspects of his meditations that I had learned from other traditions, but Drunvalo taught his practices in the most beautiful and refreshing way. Plus, he radiates a pure love and genuineness that is instantly palpable to anyone who meets him. Interspersed with the guided meditations were fun activities that allowed us to shift into a deep state of love, gratitude, and connection within all our hearts. I loved everything about this workshop.

Then during one of the heart meditations, a sudden vision appeared within my inner awareness. It was a series of flashing images of that office space near Golden Gate Park!

Have you ever seen those cartoon picture flip-books? The vision was a bit like that.

Scene by scene, frame by frame, I was shown the most incredible transformation. The boring space with drab white walls, boxes, and shelves turned into a beautiful healing oasis that made my heart soar! All the colors, the walls, the plants, and the exact layout was shown to me. With this brilliant design, there was even a special community space where group classes, movie nights, and wellness events could take place. In the vision, inspirational speakers and teachers from around the world would come to teach and share their empowering messages with my community.

It was unbelievable. I was being shown the future of my dreams! Tears of gratitude began rolling down my cheeks.

Next came a vision of myself chatting with the owner of the building, with complete authenticity about who I was, my mission, my passion, and my purpose. There would be no negotiation. I would be completely transparent about my finances and go straight to offering him my max budget. No trying to "lowball and meet half-way" or any such traditional negotiation tactics. I would fearlessly "go all in" and allow him to decide.

The meditation left me with a great feeling of clarity, optimism, and a calm confidence.

That evening after the workshop, I picked up the phone and called the owner of the building. We scheduled an in-person meeting as soon as I returned to San Francisco.

To my pleasant surprise, the meeting transpired exactly as shown to me in the heart meditation. It was a literal *deja vu*! The owner of the building was an open-hearted man, and I believe he was moved by such honesty and sincerity. Within a few days, our new lease contract was signed. No negotiation. No drama. Just pure flow and ease.

When I received the keys and began creating the clinic, I followed the exact layout and design that was shown to me in the heart meditation. My budget was impossibly small; I didn't know exactly how we could pull it all off. But a village of generous friends and angels lent their helping hands at the perfect moments. They made the impossible possible! (To our village of angels - THANK YOU!) The space turned out every bit as beautiful as in the vision - all done on time and on budget. If you've ever opened a brick-and-mortar business in a commercial space, you know what a miracle that is!

Through the assistance of many hands seen and unseen, the new Dan Tian Wellness Center of San Francisco was born. At our grand opening, the fresh paint was still drying. I stood there in awe at the magic and mystery of it all.

Since then, we've been blessed to share our healing sanctuary with thousands of people through individual sessions and group workshops. We've facilitated hundreds of transformative events, including all the live SuperWellness classes, which ultimately led to the birth of this book that you now hold in your hands. Without the blessing of this special space, SuperWellness might not have been created with such ease and grace.

To this day, the engineer in me still wonders how it's possible that the Heart could perceive beyond time and space, and how it can communicate messages to me in such a powerful way. But no amount of disbelief would ever change the fact that it happened.

The Heart has Superpowers.

LET OUR HEART BE THE BOSS

For some time after that 2011 experience, I censored myself from sharing this strange and mysterious backstory of our clinic space. My math and engineering mind found it too inexplicable. Most of my life, I had been highly trained at analyzing facts and figures as the gold standard for decision making. That's the normal way of doing things, right?

Then one day, I saw this quote attributed to Albert Einstein:

"The intuitive mind is a sacred gift, and the rational mind is a faithful servant. We have created a society that honors the servant and has forgotten the gift."

Wow! Could it be, that Albert Einstein was tapped into the same experience that I discovered in my heart meditation? Was this the key to his genius?

Upon further research, I realized that this way of following the heart's intuitive intelligence is extremely common amongst the world's most highly successful leaders. The more I researched, the more I found that successful pioneers in every industry credit **"listening to and aligning with their heart"** as the key to true long-term success.

Here are Oprah's words of wisdom:

"When you don't know what to do, do nothing. Get quiet so you can hear the still, small voice - your inner GPS guiding you to true North."

Steve Jobs shared:

"Don't let the noise of others' opinions drown out your own inner voice. Most importantly **have the courage to follow your heart and intuition.** *They somehow already know what you truly want to become. Everything else is secondary."*

Peter Diamandis, founder of the XPrize (named one of the world's top 50 leaders by Fortune Magazine) said:

"Anything I do has got to be truly from the heart and the soul… *If love isn't there, it's never going to thrive. Unless you love, love, love what you do…, unless you're driven by that internal 'massively transformative purpose', heart and soul - you're going to give up before you succeed."*

Maya Angelou said:

"The heart is the only thing we can trust."

"I believe the heart is the most forceful, impactful element in our lives."

Wow. If Albert Einstein, Oprah Winfrey, Steve Jobs, Peter Diamandis, and Maya Angelou are all tapping into this intuitive heart, then perhaps it's not something we should relegate only to the spiritual "new-agey" circles. Instead, it is a practical tool for success, joy and fulfillment.

This may be the secret to accessing our greatest human potential.

As I gave myself permission to practice "living from the heart" over the years, I've come to see this as **the most practical, sensible, and natural way to live**.

In the past, if I had an important decision, I would start by writing out long lists of pros and cons. I would look at all the facts, figures, and Excel spreadsheet models to make the best decision.

Today, the first thing I do before a big decision is get still and go within my heart, allowing it to guide me through visions, sensations, and feelings first. Informed by this guidance and clarity, I then use my brain power and analytical skills to work out all the logistical details. I notice that when decisions are informed by the heart's intuitive guidance <u>first</u>, and analytical brainpower <u>second</u>, life always seems to flow more smoothly and effortlessly.

In other words, **my "heart-mind" is the "big boss", and my "brain-mind" is "second-in-command"**, rather than the other way around.

As we'll discover later in this chapter, the heart has always been the "big boss" in our human physiology, but science has just started to understand this in the past 2.5 decades. There is much more I'd like to share with you about the scientific research around "heart-based living" and how it impacts our health and physiology.

But before we dive into the research, let's give you a direct experience of it first. Our next SuperWellness Lab is many people's favorite meditation in the entire program. I hope you love it too!

SUPERWELLNESS LAB - HEART MEDITATION FOR INTUITIVE GUIDANCE

In your Chapter 8 book bonuses, there's a special guided meditation that I created for you, synthesizing elements that I learned from a variety of different teachers. This meditation is designed to bring you into the experience of your heart's intuitive intelligence and gain greater clarity.

Note: for smaller day-to-day decisions (e.g.: *"should I go to this party or that one?"*, *"should I eat Indian or Thai food for dinner?"*), I use the "Truth vs. Falsehood Body Test" that you learned in Chapter 7.

When it comes to life's bigger decisions (e.g.: relationships, moving to a new city, whether or not to have a second child, business partnerships, etc.), I like to use this Heart Meditation to listen to the heart for inner guidance and clarity.

Here is a brief introduction of this SuperWellness Lab Heart Meditation:
1. First, choose an area of your life for which you need greater clarity. For the purpose of this exercise, simplify the situation down to two options: Option A vs. Option B. Keep this in mind before you begin the guided meditation.
2. The meditation will guide you into an experience of deep appreciation, gratitude, love, and connection within your heart. (Full details within

the video.) This becomes a new reference point, a feeling that we use as our "inner GPS."

3. When that part of the meditation is complete, you'll be invited to bring up your decision - Option A vs. Option B. You will imagine these two options as spheres that you hold in your two hands. You will bring them right up against your heart one-at-a-time and <u>feel</u> into the two choices. (The video will provide exact details.)

    The intuitive heart communicates through feelings, sensations, and visions, whereas the analytical mind communicates through thoughts, words, or intellectual arguments. If ever the heart speaks through words, it's a very gentle whisper accompanied by a joyful loving feeling. So the <u>feeling</u> is the key.

4. At the end of the meditation, come back to your center, to your natural state of peace and gratitude, and then take a few moments to jot down the wisdom and insights in your journal. Take your time to gently ease back to life.

Visit www.SuperWellness.com/BookBonuses/ and play the Heart Meditation video in your Chapter 8 book bonuses. Find out why it's many people's favorite. Enjoy!

<u>WARNING</u>: **this meditation guides you into a deeply relaxed meditative state. Do not listen while driving or operating heavy machinery.**

JUMPING BETWEEN MEDICAL PARALLEL REALITIES

Back in my early days training to become a Chinese Medicine Doctor, I always felt a strange push-pull going from our Western Medicine classes to our Eastern Medicine classes. It was as if I was jumping back and forth between two different parallel realities. If you've ever explored Eastern Energy Medicines or Eastern Philosophies, I'm sure you can relate to this.

In order to study Western physiology, pharmacology, and Western internal medicine, I would turn on my linear, Cartesian, and dualistic brain. Everything in our Western medicine classes was presented as black-and-white, linear, and mechanistic.

Then an hour later in Chinese Medicine class, I would have to switch to a completely different mindset, jumping to a parallel reality where everything is interconnected and nothing can be truly separated. My thinking had to become <u>hugely expanded</u> and flexible like a Daoist - nonlinear, non-dualistic, and multi-dimensional. It's the only way one can understand the holistic worldview of Chinese Medicine.

As students, we were required to constantly jump back and forth between these two parallel realities. It felt like I had split personalities! I yearned to integrate the worlds of East and West. It didn't make sense to me that the two models of reality could be so different.

For example, in Western Medicine class they would talk about how the autonomic nervous system (ANS) was called "autonomous" because its activities are all "involuntary" and could not be consciously controlled. Then, in our Qigong and Tai Chi classes, we would all have the <u>direct experience</u> of consciously influencing our autonomic nervous system, doing exactly what the physiology textbook said was impossible!

Which one is true? Our experience? Or the textbooks?

That's why I leapt for joy when the 2014 study with the group of Wim Hof students was published in Proceedings of the National Academy of Science, demonstrating scientifically for the first time, that the autonomic nervous system is not actually "autonomous." The new science is now catching up with our direct experience! [85]

When it came to the physiology of the **human heart**, these two models of reality presented to us by Western vs. Chinese Medicine textbooks couldn't be further apart. It left me feeling confused for years.

In the Western physiology textbooks, we were taught that the heart is a physical pump that circulates blood throughout the body. Its function is entirely controlled by the brain. The cardiovascular centers within the brain stem signals to the heart through the vagus nerve.

In other words, the **heart is a pump which is directed by the brain.** End of story.

But in daily life, we humans instinctually point to our hearts when we are pointing towards ourselves. Why is it that we always emphasize the importance of our heart in our culture and language? E.g.: "put your heart into it", or "what a good-hearted person!" or "that guy has such a big heart!" Intuitively, I think we can all feel that the heart is far more central to our health and our lives than the textbooks have told us.

In contrast to the Western textbooks, for thousands of years Chinese Medicine maintained that **the heart is the "emperor" that directs all the body's physiological functions**. In other words, the heart is the #1 organ which influences everything else. Its responsibility goes far beyond just a physical pump. Every organ of the human body is thought to be directed by the heart. The word "heart" ("xin") is also interchangeable with the word "mind" in English. In other words, from the Chinese Medicine perspective, the heart and mind are one and the same! So the word "xin" is often translated into English as "heart-mind."

The Chinese Medicine literature also emphasizes how the heart is prone to injury by emotional stress. Therefore minimizing emotional stress and maintaining a calm and peaceful "heart-mind" is of fundamental importance to our overall health.

For example, in 110 BC, it was written in one medical text:

> *"**The heart is the ruler of all organ networks**. It commands the movements of all four extremities. It circulates Qi and Blood. It bridges the realms of the material and the immaterial, and it is in tune with the gateways of every action."* [86]

In 1570, a Ming Dynasty doctor wrote:

> *"The ancients referred to the **heart as the ruler of the entire human body, the seat of consciousness and intelligence**. If we decide to nourish this crucial element in our daily practice, then our lives will be long, healthy, and secure. If the ruler's vision becomes distracted and unclear, however, the path will become congested, and severe harm to the material body will result. If we lead lives that are centered around distracting thoughts and activities, harmful consequences to our health will result."* [87]

In 1575, another medical text emphasized the energetic and spiritual functions of the heart, beyond the physical organ:

> *"The heart is the master of the body, and the emperor of all organ networks.* **There is a physical/structural heart made from blood and flesh...** *situated underneath the lung and above the liver.* **There is also a luminous energetic heart of the spirit** *(called "shen" in chinese) which generates the Qi and Blood and thus is the root of life. It is the source of all our bodily parts and functions, yet it does not manifest in obvious signs and colors.... Despite its elusive nature, this heart-spirit-"shen" commands our body's every action and every part. Material form and the luminous heart-shen-spirit must therefore be looked upon as an interdependent pair. We have to understand that diseases of the structural heart are always caused by unbalanced emotions such as depression, anxiety, obsession, or sadness, which open up pathways through which pathogenic illness can enter."* [88]

When I studied all of this in Chinese Medicine school, it felt wise and deeply resonant. But the engineer in me thought: *"Those are just nice poetic words. How much of this is scientifically true?"*

Then in 2011, when I attended Drunvalo Melchizedek's Heart Meditation workshop, it all clicked! Drunvalo introduced us to the latest scientific research at **The HeartMath Institute** with fascinating new discoveries about the physiology of the human heart.

It turns out the ancient Chinese Medical texts were really onto something. The latest scientific research now shows that the heart does in fact have power to direct every physiological function. The energetic state of the heart influences all systems of the human body. It can even influence the state of other people around us!

These findings are rewriting the textbooks and awakening a whole new realm of human possibilities.

A NEW PHYSIOLOGY OF THE HUMAN HEART

Have you heard of **The HeartMath Institute** in California?

Over the past 26 years, HeartMath has been pioneering a new understanding of the physiology of the human heart. The results have exciting and far reaching consequences regarding our human potential and our ability to influence our own health, our communities, and the world!

It turns out that the heart is far more complex, elegant, and intelligent than just a mere physical pump that receives directives from the brain. Researchers have found that the communication between the heart and the brain actually goes <u>both</u> ways.[89]

Below are just some of the fascinating discoveries by HeartMath:

- The heart is constantly sending messages to the brain, with powerful influence on our overall physiology, health, and performance.

- The heart communicates to the brain in four major ways:

    1. Neurologically through nerve impulses
    2. Biochemically through hormones and neurotransmitters
    3. Biophysically through pressure waves
    4. Energetically through the heart's electromagnetic field

- Did you know that the heart is a hormone gland?

- Scientists and physicians now consider **"heart rate variability" (HRV)**, or the variations in the beat-to-beat interval of heartbeats, to be an important indicator of health and fitness. As a marker of physiological resilience and behavioral flexibility, HRV reflects our ability to adapt effectively to stress and environmental demands. (source: heartmath.com) This adaptability sounds a whole lot like our "definition of health" from Chapter 3, doesn't it?

- Having abnormally low HRV for one's age group is associated with increased risk of future health problems and premature mortality.

- Researchers discovered an optimal healthy state known as **"Heart Coherence"** in which there is a smooth rhythmic, orderly and harmonious synchronization among various systems in the body including the heart, brain, respiratory system, blood pressure, etc.. In this state, all systems work at their optimal efficiency and performance skyrockets. (Those ancient Chinese texts were really onto something after all!)

- This measureable state of "heart coherence" is a more precise physiological definition of what has long been termed the high performance "flow state."

- Rhythmic breathing, gratitude practice, and a variety of other self-care practices can assist us in shifting into our optimal "heart coherence/flow state".

- At the HeartMath Institute, they've designed an intentionally simple set of meditation and visualization techniques, along with biofeedback devices, so that this state can be easily accessible to anyone. Their techniques have been thoroughly tested, measured, and scientifically validated to help people of all ages (including children) shift into their optimal state of heart coherence.

- This means that the high performance "flow state" can now be accessed consciously by anyone who chooses to practice the heart coherence techniques.

- The state of heart coherence is associated with greater emotional regulation, lower stress, greater peace and relaxation, access to clarity, feeling of being centered and connected, elimination of distraction, and ability to focus on what is important. Who doesn't want that?

- Using heart coherence techniques:
    o Heart patients have shown improved cardiac function and blood pressure, lower stress and cortisol, and reduced health care costs!
    o Middle school students with ADHD improved their short- and long-term memory, ability to focus, and improvements in home and school behavior
    o Fighter pilots demonstrated improved performance and lower stress levels
    o Soldiers with PTSD demonstrated improved cognitive function

- o Correctional officers had lower blood pressure, cholesterol, glucose, stress, anger, hostility, frustration and fatigue.
- In fact, HeartMath's techniques have been found to benefit patients with many types of chronic health conditions. This includes: hypertension, arrhythmia, metabolic disorders like diabetes, autoimmune disorders, environmental sensitivity, sleep disorders, drug and alcohol addiction, anger, heart failure, chronic pain, fibromyalgia, chronic fatigue syndrome, anxiety disorders, depression, PTSD, ADD/ADHD, eating disorders, and many more.
- The state of heart coherence has been shown to increase our access to intuitive intelligence. (Could this be the reason why my 2011 heart meditation unfolded in such a strange and magical way?)
- This one blew my mind the most: the heart's electromagnetic field may have a direct influence on the epigenetic expression of our DNA! [90]

Doc Childre, the founder of HeartMath, postulates that:

"The heart serves as a key access point through which information originating in the higher dimensional structures is coupled into the physical human system (including DNA), and that states of heart coherence generated through experiencing heartfelt positive emotions increase this coupling."

Wow. That sounds a whole lot like what the ancient Chinese Medical texts described!

Are you surprised that optimizing the energetic state of your heart can have such massive and far reaching consequences across all aspects of our health?

But the benefits of heart coherence go far beyond just the individual level. It turns out that heart coherence increases feelings of connection amongst groups of people, which improves group collaboration and teamwork. It is as if there's an unseen intuitive connection between members of the team, where there is greater energetic coherence and unspoken intuitive communication.

FROM "PERSONAL COHERENCE" TO "SOCIAL COHERENCE" TO "GLOBAL COHERENCE"

Have you ever noticed how, when a warm-hearted person with a harmonious energy walks into a room, the entire energy of the room seems to shift?

Research at the HeartMath Institute suggests that when one person is in a state of heart coherence, he/she radiates a measurable electromagnetic field associated with the coherent state, which influences others to also shift into their heart coherence as well.

In other words, our personal coherence enhances everybody around us and creates "social coherence." This "social coherence" effect has been found in studies involving adults, children, babies, even pets and animals. This suggests that everything you've been doing to cultivate your personal wellness can have (or has had!) a powerful energetic influence on your friends, family and community!

By cultivating your personal well-being, you naturally become that wonderfully warm-hearted person that walks into the room and shifts the entire energy of the room. Through the unseen (but palpable) energetic communications between all our hearts, everybody around you will naturally level up when you level up. And you don't have to do anything special, except be your most healthy and natural self.

Isn't that wonderful? Everybody wins!

BUT WAIT, THERE'S MORE!

Research shows that as more people join together in the state of heart coherence, not only do small groups of people shift, the entire world can shift.

At the Institute of Science, Technology and Public Policy, over 50 demonstration projects and 23 published scientific articles have shown that when a group of people bring their hearts together and meditate on peace, violent crime rates and terrorism drops down dramatically. (source: PermanentPeace.org)[91]

One famous study in Washington D.C., enrolled a group of experienced meditators to meditate on peace in a coordinated way from June 7th to July 30rd in 1993. The number of participants began with 800 and increased to 4000 by the end of the study. The results? There was a 23.3% drop in violent crimes that year! The Chief of Police exclaimed that he had never seen anything like it. He believed the only thing that could create a 20% drop in crime would be 20 inches of snow! But the project took place during blistering summer weather when crime rate is usually high. (source: WorldPeaceGroup.org)[92]

In a two-year study, a group of 7000 meditators were gathered to meditate on peace and with an intention for reducing global terrorism. They assembled for three separate week-long meditation gatherings, interspersed throughout a two year study period. Can you guess the results? During those three distinct periods of coordinated meditations, there was a 72% reduction in injuries or fatalities from terrorism across the globe! This 72% measurement is after ruling out all possible reduction that was due to pre-existing cycles, trends, or seasonal changes. 72 percent! (source: PermanentPeace.org)[93]

With an ever growing body of research, the evidence is now overwhelmingly convincing that our human intention and group consciousness can have a powerful influence on the world.

Research has even found that a group of meditators joining hearts and minds together to meditate on peace may have an exponential effect - i.e. ten people joining together in a common intention for peace will have not only a 10x effect of one person, but rather a 100x effect! [94]

Based on these studies, research scientists have predicted that if only 1% of our world population meditates on a consistent daily basis on world peace, the entire world could shift. [95]

AS YOU SHIFT, THE WHOLE PLANET SHIFTS - LITERALLY!

As if all of the above is not mind-blowing enough, there's more! The research now suggests that it's not just people and societies that are influenced by our heart coherent state. The Earth herself may be influenced by it too!

At the HeartMath Institute, the latest research is now studying how our human intention can influence the earth's geomagnetic field. It has long been known that the earth's magnetic field can influence our human energy and emotional states. But now, through a project called "The Global Coherence Initiative", the Institute has installed a set of sensors all around the globe to measure the earth's geomagnetic activity. Evidence suggests that our human energy fields may have a significant impact on the earth's magnetic resonance as well.

In other words, you are a truly powerful creator! Your consciousness and your state of being can have a dramatic influence on the well-being of your friends, your family, your community, humanity, and even the Planet Earth herself!

In the previous chapter, we introduced the idea that when we change ourselves from inside out, the whole world can change. Now, with our new understanding from HeartMath Institute and the Peace Meditation studies, it adds undeniable scientific evidence that - **when you shift yourself from inside out, the whole world shifts.**

"For my ally is the force, and a powerful ally it is." ~Yoda.

Yes my friend. Use the force! Powerful being you are!

As we complete this chapter, I'd like to recommend a phenomenal documentary exploring this power and intelligence of our hearts. It's called *"The Power of the Heart."* Have you seen it?

It features some of the greatest luminaries of our generation like Maya Angelou, Paulo Coelho, Deepak Chopra, Isabel Allende, Mark Nepo, Eckhart Tolle, Gary Zukav, Dr. Joe Dispenza, the researchers at HeartMath, and more. Stunning science and real-life stories are woven together with beautiful cinematography and storytelling. I have watched the film multiple times (yes it's that good) and feel confident you will love it too! www.thepoweroftheheart.com Highly recommended!

SUMMARY OF 'H' IS FOR HEART

CONGRATULATIONS! You have officially completed "Part II: The Recalibration!"

What a joy and honor to accompany you on this journey of H.E.A.L.T.H.:

- "H" is for coming Home.
- "E" is for Environment.
- "A" is for Agua and *Aaaarmph!*
- "L" is for Lightening Up.
- "T" is for Thoughts & Truth.
- "H" is for Heart-based living.

In this chapter, we dove into the fascinating new science behind "heart coherence" and cultivated a new understanding about the idea of "living from the heart."

The research is now undeniable that our heart is at the core of our health and well-being. When we cultivate our inner balance, harmony and coherence, our heart shifts into its optimal energetic state, which influences all other systems of our body to be in their most efficient and coherent state. We have greater access to intuition and experience the "flow state" where the highest levels of human performance are possible.

Not only that, our personal "coherence" can have profound ripple effects, enhancing the well-being of our friends, family, coworkers, community, and all of humanity. Our state of heart coherence may even influence Planet Earth herself!

So on behalf of SuperWellness pioneers all around the world, I want to THANK YOU for your commitment to your wellness and inner mastery. Thank you for giving the world your best self!

You are a true world-changer!

Now our journey has just one final stage. When you turn the page, you'll officially step through the portal into "Part III: The Arrival." In Part III, you'll learn exactly how to integrate and customize your own personal

SuperWellness experience. Hear directly from other SuperWellness heroes, learn the important dos and don'ts, and get yourself perfectly set up for success.

See you in "Part III: The Arrival!"

PART III: THE ARRIVAL

"Knowing is not enough, we must apply.
Being willing is not enough, we must do."

~ Leonardo da Vinci ~

WELCOME TO "PART III: THE ARRIVAL"

I t's been such an honor to share with you the best-of-the-best gems from my past 35,000+ hours of professional experience and a lifetime of research. The most empowering wellness tools and self-care strategies are now in your hands.

I hope that you feel as excited as I am about each of us becoming our own best healers. Together, let's make chronic health, happiness, and vitality the new "normal!"

Thank you for being the example of this new possibility amongst your friends, family, and in your community. Thank you for joining SuperWellness heroes all around the world in giving birth to a whole world of health and freedom.

You are a pioneer!

This section is designed to set you up for long-term success with practical examples of **how SuperWellness can be customized and applied in your life**.

In Chapter 9, we will share sample SuperWellness Recipes for common health concerns like pain, energy, weight management, allergies, and more. In Chapter 10, you'll hear inspiring stories from SuperWellness graduates about their experiences in applying this program to their lives. Finally, in Chapter 11, we'll point out some important Dos and Don'ts, so that you can have the confidence you need to implement SuperWellness and reap its greatest rewards.

Congratulations on your "arrival", my friend!

Now let's get you all set up for success!

CHAPTER 9

SuperWellness Recipes for Common Concerns

*"Neo, sooner or later you're going to realize just as I did that **there's a difference between <u>knowing</u> the path and <u>walking</u> the path.**"*

~ Morpheus in The Matrix ~

The "SuperWellness Recipes" below are designed to support you in applying and customizing your SuperWellness lifestyle in your own perfect way.

There's a saying that "knowledge is power," but that's only partly true. I think we can all agree that, in health and in life, there's an enormous difference between knowing something and implementing it. It is only through the application of the knowledge that we can truly understand and reap the rewards. Don't you agree?

Perhaps you'd like to heal faster from a health challenge. Or perhaps you're here to access your highest levels of human performance. Regardless of your background or goals, SuperWellness gives you the solid foundation for true vibrant health and lifelong well-being. As a side-effect of this healthy foundation, people often find that they recover faster from many common health concerns and experience new levels of possibilities that were previously unimaginable.

A reminder that SuperWellness does not diagnose or treat any medical conditions. Please always consult your professional healthcare provider(s) for proper diagnosis and treatment of medical concerns.

You're the boss and CEO of your own life. As you experiment with optimizing your lifestyle, you'll naturally deepen your self-awareness and find many empowering answers for yourself. As always, take only what works for you. Throw away what doesn't. It's my intention that the "SuperWellness Recipes" below will serve as inspiration and a quick start guide. Enjoy, and cheers to your success!

SUPERWELLNESS RECIPE FOR SUPERCHARGING YOUR ENERGY

In my experience, common causes of low energy include: poor breathing, stagnant energy flow (e.g. sitting all day), chronic dehydration, lack of sunshine, lack of sleep, an out-of-balance ungrounded electrical state in the body, over commitment and allowing the world to pull us into distractions, eating too much too fast, and stressful thoughts and emotions. Below are my top eight recommendations for supercharging your energy that you can implement - today!

- **Daily Deep Breathing & Qigong Meridian Patting Exercise**
  Oxygenate your body and move your Qi! (See Chapter 3 book bonus video.)
- **Hydration - drink the best quality water, and create EZ Water.**
  (See Chapter 5 "A" is for Agua.)
- **Sunshine during the day**
  (See Chapter 4 "E" is for Environment.)

- **Sleeping in Darkness at night**

  (See Chapter 4 "E" is for Environment.)

- **Grounding/Earthing regularly**

  (See Chapter 4 "E" is for Environment.)

- **Eating Slowly and Mindfully**

  Decrease stress on digestive system (See Chapter 6 "L" for Lightening up.)

- **Simplifying your life; cultivating a practice of saying 'no' to distractions.**

  What situations, projects, or people are distracting you from your own priorities, or causing you to feel drained? Can you cultivate the skill of saying 'no' to these distractions, which is really saying 'yes' to yourself? Is it time for a digital detox? (See Chapter 6 "L" for Lightening up.)

- **Gratitude, forgiveness, and letting go of stressful thoughts**

  (See chapter 3 on gratitude and chapter 7 on mind-body connection.)

  Interesting factoid - Did you know? Forgiveness has been found to enhance vertical jumping heights and decrease perceived effort in uphill running?[96]

SUPERWELLNESS RECIPE FOR PAIN

Pain can be caused by a variety of underlying factors, including medical conditions for which you should seek prompt professional medical attention. But there is a fundamental element of inflammation across all cases. The key is to understand and address the root causes of chronic inflammation and support the body's own natural anti-inflammatory, healing, and regenerative functions.

- **Deep Breathing is #1 for pain**

  Deep Breathing floods your body with oxygen and helps to remove inflammatory toxins and metabolic waste through the exhalation. (See also Chapter 7 on Dr. John Sarno's "Tension Myositis Syndrome" which is a state of low-grade oxygen deprivation.) Breathing not only oxygenates tissues, it can shift your pH level to a more alkaline state, which alters the experience of pain. Breathing can also shift your nervous system into the state of peace and relaxation in which optimal healing can occur. (Please see your Chapter 3 book bonuses.)

- **Dr. E says *"Move Your Qi!"* (use Qigong Meridian Patting daily)**

  In Chinese Medicine, pain is associated with stagnation of circulation. There's a saying: *"Where there's pain, there's blockage. Without blockage, there's no pain."* So it is recommended to move your body to the degree that you can, without aggravating any pre-existing injury. Movement supports healthy circulation, which allows oxygen and nutrients to be delivered to the tissues that need it the most. If you're injured, please listen to your body and work with a professional to find creative, gentle, and safe ways to "Move your Qi!" (See Chapter 3 book bonuses for Qigong Meridian Patting.)

- **Hydration - drink plenty of fresh clean water**

  Dehydration can decrease the body's ability to manage inflammation. Drink the best quality water that you can access, and experiment with enhancing your "EZ Water" which supports optimal cellular and physiological function. (See Chapter 5 "A" is for Agua.)

- **Grounding/Earthing**

  Physical contact with the earth supplies the body with abundant negative electrons, which has been shown to balance the body's electricity and reduce inflammation and pain. (See Chapter 4 "E" is for Environment.)

- **Sleeping in darkness at night**

  The darkness hormone melatonin has potent anti-inflammatory benefits and supports tissue healing and repair. (See Chapter 4 "E" is for Environment.)

- **Sunshine during the day**

  Vitamin D has been found to optimize our immune system and reduce inflammation. But there is also evidence that UV light can enhance circulation and cardiovascular function, which helps to decrease blockages in the flow of energy and enhance the flow of nutrients to support tissue healing. (See Chapter 4 "E" is for Environment.)

- **Food - experiment and find your optimal F.A.N. diet**

  Experiment with your foods, and/or work with a professional practitioner to determine which foods may be causing chronic inflammation in your system. (See Chapter 5 "A" is for *Aaaarmph!* for my top five list of allergenic/inflammatory foods.)

- **Reduce Stress - what are your favorite stress-busting tools?**

  For many people suffering from chronic pain, this may be the single greatest difference-maker. (See Chapter 7 "T" is for Thoughts & Truth - on the power of our mind-body connection.)

SUPERWELLNESS RECIPE FOR ALLERGIES

In conventional western medicine, allergies are generally thought to be caused by an "overproduction of histamines." So the most common treatment is antihistamines, along with the avoidance of allergic triggers. Chinese Medicine takes a broader approach which focuses on overall balance and harmony, seeing symptoms as a cry for better balance, rather than "the body is making a mistake." Besides decreasing excessive irritants and alleviating the symptoms, it seeks to build up the body's natural ability to adapt, self-regulate, and harmonize with environmental factors.

According to Chinese Medicine, and in my clinical experience, the vast majority of allergy patients are not only suffering from excessive exposure to irritants, but also a deficiency in many important immune-related factors. These deficiencies are not to be overlooked! When the deficiencies are addressed, we often see an improved ability for the body to self-regulate its response to environmental factors. Beyond minimizing your exposure to allergens or irritants, below are my top five tips for assisting with allergies.

- **Hydration - drink more fresh clean water!**

  Healthy hydration ensures that your mucous membranes are moist and well-hydrated, which gives your body a helpful buffer from allergenic irritants. Dehydration makes blood, lymph, and mucous more sticky and congested, which causes further irritation and inflammation. (See Chapter 5 "A" is for Agua for guidelines on drinking the best quality water.)

- **Work with a health practitioner to address vitamin or nutrient deficiencies.**

  Common deficiencies amongst my allergy patients include Vitamin D, B12, Folate, Zinc, and Vitamin C. Iron deficiency anemia is also common amongst women (more than men). All of this can be addressed with appropriate supplementation, but the correct dosage can vary hugely between individuals. So please work with your health practitioner for appropriate blood work and to optimize your dosage.

- **Get the Best Quality Sleep, in Complete Darkness.**

  Nearly all my allergy patients have noticed that their symptoms are aggravated by sleep deprivation. Are you sleeping well? Sleeping enough? (See Chapter 4 "E" is for Environment.)

- **Watch the "Sinus-clearing Acupressure" Video - use as needed.**

  In your book bonuses, you'll find a special video with a sinus-clearing acupressure routine. Use it as needed to decrease congestion and keep the sinuses clear. (See Chapter 3 book bonuses, part of the Breathing & Qigong series.)

- **Fine-tune your F.A.N. diet, eliminate the top five most aggravating foods.**

  When the body is chronically irritated by inflammatory foods, then we may be more prone to a hyper-reactive response to additional irritants. In my own life, eliminating wheat, milk, sugar, and all processed foods gave me the greatest relief from my seasonal allergy symptoms. Since then, I've found similar results with countless allergy patients. When we avoid the aggravating factors that we <u>do</u> have control over, then the body has a greater capacity to harmonize with the aggravating factors that we <u>don't</u> have control over. So if you're suffering from allergies, I encourage you to make it a high priority to optimize your F.A.N. diet. (See Chapter 5 "A" is for Aaaarmph!)

- **Reduce Stress.**

  Our stress levels influence our immune function in profound ways. Many of my allergy patients find great relief by making it a priority to reduce their stress. (See Chapter 7 "T" is for Thoughts & Truth.)

SUPERWELLNESS RECIPE FOR GETTING THE PERFECT BODY!

When it comes to weight loss and creating your ideal body, the principles are actually no different from overall health! Optimal weight and physique happens as a direct result of taking care of your health and well-being. Our patients and SuperWellness participants are routinely surprised to see how easily they can lose those "pesky" extra 10-15 lbs. and stay there, without deprivation, calorie counting, or rigid diet and exercise regimens. When our holistic lifestyle is optimized, we naturally shift to our ideal body weight. Plus, in this state, we radiate a bright, shiny, and vibrant energy that is always sexy and irresistible!

My tips for weight loss and getting your perfect body are below. The first three have an acronym S.S.S. - as in "Sizzling Sexy Summerbod" - not just for the summer but for all the years to come! The next three has the acronym P.O.W! So think: Sizzling Sexy Summerbod - POW!

- **Sleep is #1 - get your beauty sleep!**

  Sleep is critical for optimal health, healing, and weight loss. When we're sleep deprived, our metabolism shifts in response to the stress. Blood sugar rises, and our appetites and food cravings may increase. When we sleep plenty, it becomes far easier to make more mindful and conscious choices about all our other lifestyle habits, including food and exercise. So first get your beauty sleep, and allow many other healthy choices to unfold naturally from there. (See Chapter 4 "E" for Environment section on sleep.)

- **Sunshine**

  Have you noticed how much brighter you feel when you get adequate sunshine? Many studies now confirm how sunlight (including but not limited to just Vitamin D) helps to optimize our energy and physiology in many ways. For men, Sunshine has been shown to increase testosterone production. When we receive healthy doses of Sun (not too much, not too little), we naturally feel more glowing and radiant! (See Chapter 4 "E" is for Environment.)

- **Stress reduction**

  Are you leading a lifestyle that is packed with stress? The chronically heightened levels of cortisol in many of our bodies lead to decreased muscle-tone and increased belly fat. Is it time to recalibrate your lifestyle so that you can rest more, take care of yourself lovingly, and remove yourself from distraction and overwhelm? Consider the possibility that the extra weight is not just physical weight, but there may be emotional/psychological weight. Is it time to "Lighten Up" and simplify your lifestyle? Remember that saying 'no' to overwhelm and distractions is really saying 'yes' to your well-being! You deserve to love your life!

- **Posture**

  Consider this: even if you have the "perfect body," would you look great in a bikini with poor posture? When we hold our body in healthy alignment and good posture, our energy shifts instantly. Good posture instantly makes us look and feel brighter, more alive, more energized and happy! When it comes to improving our posture, various types of movement conditioning, Yoga, Taichi, Pilates, Feldenkrais, Alexander technique, Gyrotonics, and a variety of manual therapy techniques (e.g. Rolfing) can be of great assistance as well.

- **Oxygenation (breathing)**

  In order to be in "fat burning mode," our body needs to be well oxygenated. Anaerobic metabolism (i.e. without oxygen) is associated with an acidic pH, which sets the stage for increased inflammation. Remember that 70% of the body's toxins are eliminated through the breath. Also note that when we breathe deeply, it enhances our core strength and stability, which also assists with Posture (above). Deep breathing helps you tap into the feeling of inner strength, confidence, and stability, which naturally radiates a confidence from inside out. In my opinion, that's the definition of sexy! (See Chapter 3 on the benefits of breathing.)

- **Water**

  Consider not only the quantity, but the quality of water. Proper hydration helps to clean and detoxify the body. When we're well-hydrated, we will naturally eat lightly without any willpower or calorie counting. Not all water is the same; be sure to drink the cleanest, purest water that you can access. (See Chapter 5 "A" is for Agua.)

Sizzling Sexy Summerbod. POW!

SUPERWELLNESS PARENTING

Surprise! In your book bonuses is an extra special webinar called "SuperWellness Parenting." If you're a parent, I want to honor you for being the amazing parent that you already are! The fact that you're reading this book means that you care deeply about becoming your best self. It's clear that you are already on a journey of mastery. As we practice the SuperWellness tools, we become more vibrant, more present and connected as human beings. This is the key to parenthood, isn't it?

In this special bonus webinar, I distilled for you my top eight biggest lessons learned from 15 years of observing families in my clinical practice, in addition to my personal experience as a parent. I've been blessed to learn from many highly conscious parents in our community, witnessing how they raise their children over the years. Of special interest to me is how we as parents can share a more empowered approach to health, setting our children up for a lifetime of wellness. The eight principles in this webinar have allowed me to enjoy my own journey of parenthood with much greater confidence, joy, and ease. I hope you'll love them too!

Visit your book bonuses (www.SuperWellness.com/BookBonuses/) for the bonus webinar on SuperWellness Parenting. Enjoy!

SUPERWELLNESS RECIPE FOR SUPPORTING FRIENDS/FAMILY THROUGH A HEALTH CRISIS

Our SuperWellness community is filled with kind and deeply caring people. Many people have asked about how to best assist their loved ones through a major health challenge. Some of you maybe in a situation right now, where you are supporting a friend or family member. Or perhaps you're a professional health practitioner, who cares for patients through their health challenges on a daily basis. Below are highlights from a webinar that we hosted on this important topic.

- **Your Loving Energy and Presence Heals.**

  Often the most helpful gift during times of stress and difficulty is if one person can bring a peaceful energy to the space, isn't it true? So if you can be that person in a room who radiates a harmonious and loving energy, the entire energy of the room shifts. Remember that your energy heals, just by shifting into your own optimal "heart coherent" state. During moments of crisis or difficulty, your loving presence may be the single most helpful ingredient you can bring to the situation. (See Chapter 8 "H" is for Heart.)

- **Put yourself in the other person's shoes. Be unconditional love.**

  Consider when you've had a health challenge, what worked for you and what didn't work? In my experience, sometimes listening to everybody's mixed opinions about what to do, what not to do, can become overwhelming. I've found that what always works 100% of the time is unconditional love. *"I love you, and I'm here for you no matter what."* There's not enough of that in our world, don't you agree? Recall Anita Moorjani's story, where she credits living from the state of love (rather than fear), as the true source of her miraculous healing. So I invite you to assist your friends/family by bringing unconditional love to the healing space. (See Chapter 7 "T" is for Thoughts, "T" is for Truth.)

- **Bust the myth that there's any such thing as "incurable."**

  The human body is designed to heal and recover from the stressors of life. Spontaneous remissions have been documented in nearly every category of so-called "mysterious" or "incurable" conditions. Recall from Chapter 2 our discussion about the greatest myths. If a conventional doctor says anything is "incurable", it generally means: *"As far as I'm aware, there is not yet a known cure for this condition within drugs or surgery. So it may be appropriate to research alternatives."* Also consider Dr. Kelly Turner's research on "Radical Remissions" and all the latest science on mind-body medicine. Share this book with your friends/family and empower them with hope and inspiration. (Please see Chapter 2 The Five Great Myths and Chapter 7 "T" is for Thoughts & Truth.)

- **When major lifestyle changes are needed, how can you inspire, encourage, and support?**

  Today, the evidence is undeniable that the vast majority of our modern chronic diseases like heart disease, stroke, diabetes, obesity, etc. are related to lifestyle. But the question is, how can you inspire your friends/family to change their habits?

  By learning the principles of SuperWellness, you now have a much more holistic understanding of "healthy lifestyle" far beyond the rigid "you must eat-right-and-exercise" paradigm. In general, rather than preaching to our friends and family, I've found it far more powerful to listen, support and facilitate. Do not force your opinion on others. Simply give them space to generate their own answers with questions from you like: *"What do you think?", "What works for you?", "You know your body best. What do you think your body's needs?", "Oh I was reading this great book that changed my opinion on it. Do you want to read it too?", or "Oh I saw this great documentary and learned about this juicing cleanse. If you want to try it, I'll do it together with you!"* Can you see what a difference this kind of support could make?

  When you take beautiful care of your own health and your well-being, your example is more powerful than any words. Others around you may notice how bright, healthy, and radiant you look and feel, and they'll naturally be curious. Don't ever force your path onto others. Instead, let's take an open-hearted attitude: *"We're in this together. Here's what worked for me. Would you like to try? Let's do it together!"*

- **Celebrate milestones, and bring back the Joy and Fun!**

  During my training to become a High Performance Coach, one of the greatest keys to success that I learned is the importance of celebrating milestones. When we do not honor our hard work by acknowledging and celebrating key milestones along the way, we start to lose motivation and dread the process. On the other hand, if we celebrate regularly, we feel excited to keep going and stay consistent. So when you are assisting your friends/family through their healing journey, be sure to bring some fun, love, and joy back to the process. Point out and celebrate every milestone, so that your friends/family feel excited to continue their efforts. Sometimes managing our health can get very serious and heavy. Can you bring back the joy? Can you watch some funny movies together? Laughter and fun heals!

- ***"Health is not the absence of disease, but the ability to adapt to life's stressors and challenges."***

  Remember our discussion about "what is Health" back in Chapter 3 ("H" is for Home)? If we want to be healthy and support our friends and family to be healthy, then we must have a clear definition of "what is Health." How does a healthy person respond to illness and injury, in a way that is different from how a less healthy person may respond? How can you help your friends/family see the gifts and opportunities, beyond the pain and limitations? For clarity and inspiration, I encourage you to revisit Chapter 2's "Five Greatest Myths" and Chapter 3's discussion on "What is Health."

I hope that this chapter has been a helpful guide, giving you confidence on how SuperWellness can be customized and applied to your life. Please share your experiences, thoughts, or questions in our online forum so that we may all support one another. Our community is here for you and with you!

In the next chapter, we'll hear exciting and inspiring stories from other SuperWellness heroes in our community. They will share with us how they chose to implement SuperWellness in their own unique ways.

Find out how Zahra shifted out of injury and overwhelm into a state of spaciousness, excitement, and new possibilities. Hear the inspiring story of Marianne, as she describes how her lupus and fibromyalgia symptoms went into remission. Learn from Laurie, who found a more kind and loving way of approaching healthy lifestyle after recovering from cancer treatments. We will also discover how health professionals like Tim, Lynn, and Lisa found a more joyful and effective way of coaching their wellness clients for long-term success!

CHAPTER 10

Meet Your Fellow SuperWellness Heroes

"Your life can shift to a whole different state of possibilities. Mine did."

~ Zahra Kassam ~
Startup CEO & mother of two

I n this chapter, let's hear from some of our fellow SuperWellness heroes about their personal experiences in applying SuperWellness in their own lives.

The stories below feature interviews with graduates of our in-person or online SuperWellness programs. The views and opinions expressed are strictly those of the participant, and should never be misconstrued as medical advice, or interpreted as "typical results" or as a guarantee or prediction of outcomes for any particular issue. Because every human being has a unique journey, dependent on many factors, there's no such thing as "typical results." Please always consult a trained medical practitioner for any conditions that require professional medical attention.

A reminder that SuperWellness does not diagnose, treat, or cure any medical conditions. Instead, it is a holistic lifestyle program that helps us to cultivate a foundation for our well-being. By putting the tools and strategies in this book into action, you are choosing to take full responsibility of your own actions and results. The tools in this program should never, under any circumstance, be used as a substitute for professional medical advice or treatment. Please do not change your regimen without the careful supervision of your doctor(s).

With all that said, let's meet our fellow SuperWellness heroes! We'll hear the words of wisdom from professional health practitioners like Lisa, Tim, and Lynn, from health seekers like Melissa, Laurie, Marianne, Zahra, and from advanced "health-nuts" like Vikram and John. Their experiences are diverse, inspiring, and each uniquely beautiful. Enjoy!

LISA'S STORY

Nurse, nutritionist, and fitness coach on going beyond "Eat Right and Exercise."

Lisa: My name is Lisa Pezik. I'm from Toronto, Ontario. I worked in the intensive care unit as a nurse, and I also got into the health and fitness space where I'm a nutritionist, personal trainer, and fitness instructor. So I've coached people through both the proactive side of health, as well as the reactive side of health with my nursing background. Our health is so important! I want to instill in people this idea that we gotta take back control of our health.

Q: What inspired you take the SuperWellness course?

Lisa: It was such a different approach from anything that I experienced before. I'm a very scientifically-based, facts, figures, algorithms, and treatments-oriented person. The way that I learned about health with nursing, and also how I taught people to eat right and exercise, etc. was always very "by-the-book." But I started to realized it was almost making things too complicated for people. So I was excited about doing a validated health and wellness program that could help me simplify things. When I got into the SuperWellness course, I thought *"Wow! These are all the little things that we usually take for granted, like getting outside, breathing fresh air, practicing gratitude."* Sometimes we don't put enough merit to these simple things that can make the most dramatic shift in our health.

I was excited to learn a different approach that is beyond what I knew as a nurse and as a fitness trainer... a simpler approach that didn't involve such rigid hard-and-fast rules. Instead, learn to check in with your body and listen to yourself. That's something that I feel like we've forgotten in our world. How to be the boss of our own lives. I love the autonomy that this course taught me, and now I can share this approach with everyone in my community.

Q: Before taking the course, what reservations did you have initially?

Lisa: To be honest, my first thought was *"this is kind of woo-woo! Does this stuff really work?"* I came from a world where you have to go to the gym, or workout at home, and you have to eat these food and stay away from those foods. So I had doubts if these simple things could really work! Also I'm not a "spiritual" person; I'm not like your typical yoga person that's so in touch with your soft side. So I wasn't sure it would resonate with me, my style, my personality, etc. I wondered if this would be too woo-woo and not actually life changing.

I wanted actual things that will give me actual results!

Q: Then what tipped you over the edge to give it a try?

Lisa: Hearing the experiences and results of everyone, and how profoundly it helped them! So I told myself to open my mind to a new and different way. I think seeing how passionate Dr. Edith is, and also the physical proof in the video course. In the video course, you had a group of men, women, older people, young people, professionals, moms, dads. You had people from all walks of life. I realized, if these concepts can bring so many different types of people together, and it really works for them, then I'm silly if I don't at least give it a go!

At the end of the day, if what you're already doing is not working, then you have to switch it up. Try something different. So I decided I'll keep an open mind because Dr. Edith is so passionate and it really seems to work for people. I will give it a try!

Q: What were some challenges you've experience with your health, or challenges from your clients that were top of mind when you took the course?

Lisa: Even though I'm a trainer and a nurse, I've really struggled with emotional eating. My emotions were hard for me to deal with, and I find it's also the case with many of my clients. The issue is always so much deeper than just "lose some weight and fit into a certain size." We're really trying to find a way to heal all over – not just physical but also emotional healing.

Also I always lived by hard-and-fast rules - e.g. I have to work out every day. I can only eat from this meal plan. I have to drink this much water. It was so rigid and strict. When I was perfectly on point, it was great. But I set myself up to such a high standard that it always led to a crash. There's always the big crash and burn. You feel like a failure. Then you give up and think "why bother!" It's constant up and down waves of emotions that we create when we have this rigid "eat right and exercise" approach. I think it was too strict, too rigid, and not in tune with what my body was craving. What I really needed was to get in touch with my emotions and feel whole again, and to heal myself through positive things that aren't a meal plan or an exercise program, or the typical things that we think might bring happiness.

I realized I didn't need to lose weight. I needed to be more at peace within my life. So it was just a whole different approach. Wow! I guess I am kind of woo-woo now! (laughter) It pointed me to a whole different way that I think we can serve people.

Here's the thing: I was eating right and exercising, and losing weight, but I wasn't happy. A piece was always missing. It's the foundational stuff that you need before you can do all the eating and exercise stuff. I was taking people way up here to this level, when the real issues are down here at the foundational baseline that we never address... well, for me personally I never addressed. Things like past traumas, past emotions, past experiences.

This program just took me in a whole new direction that I never thought I was going to go. I'm so happy it did! (tears) It's true. I'm getting all emotional! So many people are struggling with their health. But we skip the most important foundation. Then all those tools up here that we're exploring are never sustainable, because it's not built on a foundation.

In my health and fitness coaching, there was always this pattern. I was getting people great results, but then 3, 4, 5 months later they say *"oh, I fell off the bandwagon."* Something felt out of alignment - just didn't sit right with me. Because I want my clients to have good health for the rest of their lives! Real longevity. What am I missing? All I ever knew was the "eat right and exercise" way, meal plans and fitness. That's why this opened my eyes to a whole different way.

Q: What was most surprising about the program?

Lisa: How <u>simple</u> things were! Now I'm not usually a negative person, but I'd watch the video course and think: *"Really? You want me to go outside and walk barefoot on the grass? Really? You want me to ask if this food is fun, and does it feel good when I'm eating? Is it that simple? Come on!"*

But it was beautiful outside. With my little guy, we would kick the soccer ball and run around with bare feet in the grass. Or I'd garden without the gloves and get my hands in the dirt. I had this incredible sense of energy and peace. I felt so grounded. I guess that's why they call it grounding! (laughter) I was blown away. Something so simple as taking your shoes off and laying on the grass. It's just a beautiful way to connect with yourself and connect with nature. It completely flipped my mindset.

The same thing with food. *"Is it Fun? Does it make you feel Alive?"* You just ask yourself these simple questions as opposed to: *"I can eat this, I can't eat that. It's bad, it's good. Oh that one I can only have on this occasion… etc."* There are so many rules that over-complicate things. I think just the simplicity of it all, even talking to my water… it opened my eyes to all the things that I have to be thankful for - the roof over my head, the love of my family, the abundance of clean water we have. I realized, sometimes I'm so focused on what I don't have that I'm not seeing all the things I do have. It made me a much more peaceful and grounded person.

It always goes far beyond what the concept seems at first. For example, with the water, it wasn't just about talking to your water, but being grateful for your life! It's not about putting my feet in the grass, but feeling connected with my son and having a different experience in my life - this gratitude, happiness, and energy. There are such beautiful gifts, that if I didn't have an open mind to try it, I would have never experienced them. So it was all very surprising to me.

Another big surprise was the juicing/fasting. I tried fasting so many times in the past, but I realize now that I never succeeded because I didn't have my mindset right. I thought, if I can't get through the whole day, then I forget it! But with SuperWellness, because we do so much work leading up that lesson where we do the juice fast, my mindset was ready for that experience. And it felt amazing! It was so easy to do because I had the right foundation. I realize that I can do anything when my mindset is right.

Q: Wow! What were your top three favorite tools from the SuperWellness course?

Lisa: I love the grounding. I still do that regularly. I love the Byron Katie work. Those questions were very transformational for me. I love asking the questions around the F.A.N. diet. Making things so simple. And I LOVE the ending of the course, getting in tune with your heart. What your heart wants and needs, and just being in touch with yourself. For me, I'm such a go go go go person that I rarely stop to think - is this making me happy?

There were so many great tools! The breathing too! I love the Qigong and all the physical activities. It only takes five minutes a day. There was not one single thing in the course where I thought - *"this is going to take too much time, it's too difficult to fit into my schedule."* Everything takes seconds or a few minutes. And my whole day is changed from doing these simple things.

Q: Who do you feel SuperWellness is for, and who is it not for?

Lisa: I think it is <u>definitely</u> for anyone in the healthcare, fitness, or nutrition industries. Anyone who is a healer, or wants to heal themselves.

SuperWellness is a must for everyone in the fitness or nutrition industry because we have to start looking at alternative ways of reaching people. They are not getting the success long-term because they don't have the right foundation.

It's also for people who are at the point of frustration with their health and are ready for a better way. It's for anyone who's willing to trust the process, and trust that you can be your own healer. You can be the boss of your own body. You can tune into these emotions, as scary as it might be in the beginning. When you do the work, you'll feel so much better for it.

SuperWellness is not for people who are cynical and don't have an open mind to try different things. I think if you're a very closed minded person, you need to do some other work so that you can go into this course with an open mind.

So SuperWellness is for anyone who has an open mind and really wants change, or if they're in the healthcare industry - fitness, nutrition, physios, chiropractors - anyone who touches people and helps them with their health, this course is a necessity. It's a must. It's the foundational stuff that we all need.

Q: Final words of wisdom for readers who are struggling with their health?

Lisa: Don't overcomplicate things. Go back to that daily check-in: e.g. What gratitude do I have? Am I breathing? Am I moving? Am I connected? Am I present? Am I checking in with myself and how I feel? Am I keeping an open mind that if I do the simple foundational things, I can feel better?

There are no hard-and-fast rules here. When you tune in, you already know what your body needs. Tune into yourself. Trust the process. There are things that you'll never expect you'll experience. But if you do this deeper level stuff, you'll feel so much better. It's something that you can sustain. It doesn't have to be complicated. All the resources to heal yourself are there. You might want to use other tools too! But this is how you start. Build the foundation. Start here. It's amazing.

ZAHRA'S STORY

Busy mom and startup entrepreneur avoids surgery and shifts into whole new state of possibilities.

Zahra: My name is Zahra Kassam. I'm the founder of Monti Kids. I was previously a Montessori preschool teacher. I had my first child five years ago and was trying to create an educational environment for him at home, right from birth, and it was really difficult. So that's why I started my company Monti Kids to help parents do that. I have a very busy life with a startup, we're at seven employees now, and I have a five year old. Plus I'm now pregnant with our second baby. A lot going on!

Q: Tell us what attracted you to the SuperWellness program.

Zahra: I was in a rough place when I found out about SuperWellness. Because I have my startup, and this was before we were seven employees, there were only a few of us. I had been working on the startup for a few years all by myself. The nonstop typing on the computer led me to develop a lot of pain in my hands, wrists, elbow, and shoulders. I really couldn't use my hands much anymore. But I couldn't stop because I couldn't just suddenly drop my startup.

I was getting very disillusioned and almost depressed about my whole life. I felt like I was doing way too much, trying to start a company, and also trying to be an involved mother. It was so hard; I'd feel guilty at work for not spending enough time with my son. Then I'd feel guilty when I was with my son, because I wasn't working enough. So I wasn't enjoying it. I felt like I needed a drastic change in my lifestyle, I needed to improve my health – my physical, mental, and emotional health. So honestly, it was out of desperation that I took SuperWellness.

Q: Before SuperWellness, what did you try that helped or didn't help?

Zahra: The problem I was most concerned about was the debilitating pain in my hands and wrists. I had been to my conventional doctor who, quickly without spending much time, just told me it was carpal tunnel. But I read a lot about carpal tunnel, and the diagnosis didn't seem correct. She recommended Physical Therapy, which I did, but it didn't help. Then they recommended I wear splints, which led to tennis elbow, and on and on. It was all getting worse, not better. Then I was recommended to see a hand surgeon, who again without spending time with me just recommended I do the Carpal Tunnel Surgery. The attitude was *"Well, try the surgery, and we'll see if it doesn't work."* But it just didn't feel right to jump into surgery so nonchalantly!

The only thing that helped was resting. I took a break from work. But it wasn't sustainable because I had to go back to work. Even cooking for my son was difficult, I couldn't stop doing motherhood forever. It wasn't sustainable. It made me feel that my entire lifestyle was all wrong. I was desperate. Something had to change.

Q: Did you have any reservations about taking SuperWellness?

Zahra: Taking the class was quite a time commitment for me. As someone who was already feeling like "I don't have enough time to do anything," it was a huge commitment. But it was totally worth it! It turned into the most life-changing experience.

Q: Tell us about your experience with SuperWellness. Any surprises?

Zahra: It was very surprising! I was surprised how much it helped me in my overall well-being. I enjoyed connecting with the other people in the class, and hearing about their journey through health and wellness. But mostly, I really enjoyed examining those things for myself. It turned into the most life-changing experience. Sounds corny, but it's true.

The very first class where we talked about "our definition of health" was a big one for me, because of my experiences with doctors - not just with my hand pain, but also when I had my baby, when I got really sick at age 16, and all those past experiences - I always had this idea that I know myself best. Sometimes when a doctor says something, even though they're the expert, it doesn't necessarily mean it has to apply to me.

So SuperWellness validated that for me. It was a big "lightbulb" moment - the idea that I know myself best, that I can come up with my own definition of health. We should be coming up with our own definition of health and working towards that definition, and not someone else's! This can be a very holistic definition. It's not just about "eating well and exercising." There's a whole slew of other things you can do to feel well, to embody your definition of health. That was a BIG one for me.

Q: What were your biggest takeaways?

Zahra: One of the biggest takeaways I learned from the class was that I can change my state. If I wake up feeling a certain way in the morning, that doesn't mean that's how I have to feel all day. SuperWellness gave me the tools to, first of all, realize that I have the power to change my state. This was huge because sometimes you just feel like a victim, or I felt like a victim to my circumstances… vs. now realizing that I have the power, and then having these tools to go out and do it. The first time I had that experience was very, very impactful. I will not forget it – it was very powerful.

What else? I feel the class shifted me to a whole other state of well-being. I don't feel that I have to change my whole life or lifestyle. I shifted my perspective and implemented a few practices that helped me to feel really well. It made me really excited about all the things in my life again!

I started this company because I'm super passionate about it. This is what I really wanted. But somehow along the way I got so unwell that it became this negative dream in my life, and now I'm back to this state of gratitude where I LOVE my work, and I LOVE my family. There are still a lot of things going on, but they're all good things. SuperWellness shifted my state so much that my husband and I decided to have another child. We have room for lots of things in our lives, even though the circumstances haven't changed, our state of well-being has changed.

That was huge, it was a major shift. It's been many months since I graduated from the class, and this new state has not shifted back. I'm very grateful for that!

Q: What else was surprising about the class?

Zahra: The tools that sound so simple… it's surprising how impactful they are! You hear about them, and you think "*Okay, breathing, gratitude practice, and grounding can have an impact.*" It doesn't sound very powerful, but when you actually do it, and implement it, it really, really works.

Also, I was shocked that it didn't take a ton of willpower to get up and do these things every day. It's not about discipline and willpower. I have a desire to do them because they're fun and enjoyable. They have such strong effects. I think part of that shift is I have more space in my life for these things now. I've made more space because I want to, and there's an ease about it. That was very surprising.

Q: Tell us about some of your specific results, your mood, energy, aches and pains, how did those shift?

Zahra: For me, I think it was the gratitude practice in SuperWellness that changed things the most. It didn't just change my mood, it changed my perspective and my mindset about everything that was going on in my life. That coupled with the grounding, the breathing, and the Qigong practices we learned. I am a totally different person today.

It's obvious to the people around me too, how my mood has changed. I just feel excited in the morning to get out of bed, and to do all the things that I'm doing, and I feel grateful about that. I'm still very busy, but it all feels manageable - like I chose it, and not like I'm a victim of it.

In terms of energy, I have a lot more energy. It's good energy, positive energy. Plus, it's not just that my mood and energy shifted, it's that I feel self-empowered that I have control over these things now. I felt a huge lack of control about these things before I started SuperWellness.

Physically, I don't have pain anymore, but I don't know if that's SuperWellness or also seeing Dr. Edith for acupuncture, so I don't know. Hard to say. But I don't have pain anymore!

Within SuperWellness, I think probably what helped my pain the most was doing the juice cleanse, then slowly reintroducing things and seeing how my body would react. It was so much more obvious which foods were affecting my pain. There was so much I learned that I had never considered before. The fact that I can moderate my pain without surgery or physical therapy is really nice! When it comes to food, I love that it's not about self-discipline or deprivation. It's about understanding myself and appreciating my wellness. Being in charge of it. Not cutting myself off from things. Just recognizing how they make me feel, and then I naturally want to stay away from things that make me feel bad.

Q: Who do you think SuperWellness is for, and who is it not for?

Zahra: If there's anyone out there like me, who's struggling with not just a health problem but also feeling hopeless or distraught about their lifestyle, feeling *"it's too much, it's overwhelming, and something has to change!"* but they don't know where to start, I feel SuperWellness is the thing to do. Because there's nothing out there like this! It's really unique, and like I said, it's really life changing.

I think if you tried conventional practices, like diet and exercise, and seeing your doctor, and you're just frustrated with that whole process because it's not having the results you want, SuperWellness will definitely give you whole new set of tools that no one else is talking about, that are really free, simple, and remarkably effective.

I don't know who it's not for. If you're not open minded, maybe this isn't for you. If you only believe in the very conventional ways of achieving health, and you don't want to explore your own definition of health, then maybe this isn't for you.

Q: Final words of wisdom? If you were to time travel back to 1+ year ago when you were having a hard time, what would you say to yourself?

Zahra: I would say think broader and more holistically. Just because you're having pain in your hands, doesn't necessarily mean you have to jump right to a hand surgery, or even focus so much on your hands because the problem may be broader than that. There may be things out there that you haven't even considered that could dramatically change the way you're feeling.

Be open-minded to things that perhaps not everyone is talking about, but are very impactful. Take SuperWellness! It's a life changing experience that you cannot find elsewhere.

I was falling into the trap of a myth that if you're having a health problem, there are only a couple of things you can do about it. But actually there are tons more options! Not thinking broadly enough about health and only focusing on the symptoms rather than the whole situation, that's a big myth that I busted for myself.

Then, also... there was a myth that I had to change my lifestyle drastically, or that I had to stop working to get better. But it turned out I didn't have to change my lifestyle so much; I just had to change my perspective. Every time I went to a doctor they said, *"Well, you have to stop working on the computer."* I'd say, *"But I can't take months and months off work!"* A yoga therapist even told me I had to choose whether I wanted to be an involved mother or successful professional, because it just wasn't feasible to do both. I felt so angry. I wanted to say *"I don't have to choose!"* But I didn't have a good argument, because there I was, in so much pain. I didn't know a way out. Nobody was optimistic that I could do the things that I wanted to do and still be well. It felt like my lifestyle and my well-being were competing.

With SuperWellness, everything changed. I discovered I didn't have to choose anymore between being healthy and doing the things I love. I just had to think differently about it, and I introduced some simple practices that dramatically elevated my state, my energy, my well-being. Now, I'm in a state where I can do all the things I want to do and not feel pain.

SuperWellness is not an experience like other classes, where you take a lot of notes and then you put your notebook away and move on. This is a class where your whole life can shift to a different state of possibilities. Mine did.

JOHN'S STORY

Integrating the scientific and spiritual worlds into a practical experience.

Q: Please tell us your name and a bit about your background.

John: My name is John Chavez. I'm the author of *"Questions for the Lion Tamer: Delving into the Mystery that is DMT"*, a new book that just came out this year. I'm a budding entrepreneur in the space that bridges science and spirituality. I'd like to see a merging and integration of these two worlds. I had an awakening experience about four years ago, and it put me on my journey. I met Dr. Edith at a festival that she put together a few years ago, which explored the frontiers of human possibilities. I've been in touch with her since.

Q: What made you interested in the SuperWellness program?

John: I went to Dan Tian Wellness clinic and saw Dr. Edith's huge book collection at the facility and noticed a lot of overlap with what I've read, except she had a LOT more books than me! So it made me interested in seeing what she had to offer as a wellness instructor and facilitator. She has formal training as a Chinese Medicine doctor, but I also know she reads a lot outside of Chinese Medicine. I know she has distilled and simplified a ton of research within holistic wellness, and that's what I'm always looking to do also. So I was curious to see if she had anything to share that I hadn't uncovered yet. I wanted to learn.

Q: What were some challenges you had in the past with regards to your wellness?

John: Well, in the past before I got into wellness, I didn't know anything! I thought eating a Powerbar and drinking Gatorade was very healthy. I thought, *"hey, I'm not eating a Big Mac and soda."* I'd go to the liquor store and get a powerbar and Powerade. That was health to me. So I really had zero perspective on true healthy living. I had a very mainstream perspective - i.e. as long as you eat these vitamins, etc. you're gonna be healthy. If anything goes wrong, go to your local doctor and it'll all get fixed. That was my perspective until it didn't work anymore and my health started failing.

When I was about 25 years old, my health started to go downhill. Then at 32, I had a pulmonary embolism, and that's when I really started to take a deeper look at what health is. It forced me to look into what other people have experienced and how they addressed similar issues. I had a lot of digestive issues, but now I'm much better utilizing all my research and learnings, as well as tools that I've picked up from the SuperWellness course.

Q: Before taking the class, did you have any doubts or reservations about SuperWellness?

John: No reservations; I was just looking for add-ons to my existing knowledge, because I know Dr. Edith has deep knowledge on health. But I also have a decent set of knowledge. I've been able to help some friends heal from various ailments, etc. but I'm always looking to learn more. So no, I didn't have any reservations. I was just excited to see what extra tidbits I could gather.

Q: Please tell us some of your experiences. What new things did you learn? Any surprises?

John: The class where we practiced the mindful eating with the blindfold. Wow. That was very different! I had never done that before. I didn't know what to expect. Your relationship with food, slowing it down, and really focusing on bite by bite, moment to moment. That was really profound for me, especially because that day I went to the class with Marianne and knew that she was starving. But when we did that exercise, I saw how her appetite and hungers shifted. So that was very interesting to observe and witness. Also, the grounding – I had read about grounding before but hadn't implemented it consistently before. Feeling the subtle energy changes in your body was interesting.

I also learned a lot witnessing everybody's different goals and experiences in the class. All the tools in SuperWellness are so gentle, which is great because nobody had any uncomfortable healing reactions or anything like that. The way Dr. Edith lays out this gentle and thoughtful journey is really smart.

Q: What were your biggest takeaways?

John: Before, I always emphasized that to be healthy, you gotta digest well, sleep well, and eat well. But there are so many other points that Dr. Edith emphasized in the class, like the gratitude journal. Super important. It keeps you in the right frame of mind. Also conscious breathing, incorporating that throughout the day. Super important. I had researched and been cognizant of their benefits. But in taking the class, I realized it's all about doing them consistently and experiencing them, not just knowing about them.

Q: Who is SuperWellness for, and who is it not for?

John: In my opinion, SuperWellness is helpful for anyone who's had any sort of health issues. But it's not for people who feel completely skeptical of anything outside of mainstream media or mainstream medical establishment. If you have a closed mind and are unwilling to try things outside of mainstream conventional approach, then it'd be very difficult to benefit from this course.

The truth is, I think everybody should take this course and experience it. Dr. Edith explains the science behind all the tools that you're implementing. Then you have to be open to trying it and see what happens. I think anyone who is open-minded will have a great experience.

Q: Anything else you'd like to share with our readers?

John: Yes, I'm excited about SuperWellness because integrating the spiritual and scientific worlds is extremely important in my opinion. SuperWellness is a great step towards that. There's such a gap in our society between wellness and spirituality. I believe our greatest limitations have to do with our ability to access and integrate the spiritual experience.

SuperWellness creates a holistic foundation that makes spiritual awakenings possible and more accessible to everyone. That's really exciting.

Note: John and Marianne are a long-time couple who took the SuperWellness course together.

MARIANNE'S STORY

No more pain from fibromyalgia, no more flare-ups from lupus, juicing and raw vegan diet without needing willpower or discipline.

Marianne: My name is Marianne Torres. I worked as a hospice nurse for about ten years. I stopped working for some time because of my illness. I'm now back to work as a private nurse for a couple of patients. Nursing is challenging work, but I really love it.

Q: Why did you choose to take the SuperWellness course?

Marianne: John brought me to take it! I know he's a big fan of everything Dr. Edith does. So I didn't have any expectations, just to enjoy the class, and keep an open mind.

Q: Please tell us a bit about any health challenges you had in the past.

Marianne: In 2011, I was diagnosed with Lupus. But long before that, since 2001, I had symptoms of autoimmune disease in my throat. They found lumps in my neck that were being monitored with ultrasound every two years. In 2005, when I graduated from nursing school I started having issues with my reproductive system. I stopped having my periods. I gained a lot of weight and went up to 170 pounds. I was told I'd have to be on birth control pills. So I took it for six years until 2011, when my body just started giving up, and I became nearly bed bound. I had all the symptoms of Lupus, but my doctors here in the Bay Area would not diagnose me with Lupus. So I had to go to L.A., where we found a doctor who saved my life, because I was having heart failure.

I was extremely inflamed. The attacks felt like I couldn't breathe. My temperature spiked up and my hair was falling out. My color turned purple and grey. John was also having trouble with his health at that time. We were not really getting along because we were both so sick.

I was not at all in touch with my health. I would try to hide my purple and gray look and continue to go to work. But eventually people would notice my color and my hair turning gray. Driven by my superficial desire to look better and have better color, I went back to my native Philippines, where they do glutathione therapy as a cosmetic treatment for lightening the skin! I didn't know better then, I just wanted my color to look nicer. But that became a huge turning point, because with glutathione, I started feeling better and better, I noticed that I didn't have such swollen joints, and my hair was not falling out. From that experience, I realized that creating a healthy overall biochemical balance inside the body is important for my healing.

It got me thinking. Many things about my health history started to click. E.g.: when I was 18, I had a suspected thyroid goiter and got radiation for my throat. Then in my early 20s, I took a lot of antibiotics for an entire year, which I believe ended making me so sick at this age. So I realized if the glutathione antioxidant therapy was helping me feel so much better, I was probably pretty toxic inside. I starting thinking "cleanse cleanse cleanse." John and I just experimented with cleaning up our diets and taking supplements and cleaning up our bodies in various ways.

But here's where I think SuperWellness class really helped, because we had only focused on the body, eating clean and taking supplements. In SuperWellness, we look at our mind, emotions, and spiritual aspects. It all matters. It's not so narrow and rigid.

Q: What were your favorite tools and practices in the SuperWellness class?

Marianne: I really liked the interactions of the group, just knowing that everybody else also has struggles, and we can share our experiences. I learned from everybody in the group how they coped with their challenges and struggles, whether it's with their health, or just with life. I learned from everyone.

The gratitude journal practice was a huge highlight for me. I came to see many things as "blessings in disguise" and felt so thankful. If something doesn't go "right" in a moment, I always have this feeling there's something else good in store for me. Oh and the grounding practice. I always loved the feeling of being barefoot. Now it all makes sense why!

Q: What were your biggest highlights from SuperWellness class? Any surprises?

Marianne: The biggest surprise was how much I loved the Juicing! I noticed I was having cravings for grapefruit juice even before we went to SuperWellness class, so I started doing a little juicing. But then when we did the full blown juice-only days in SuperWellness for three days, it felt so great that I decided to keep going and see how it goes. So I just listened to my body and kept going for many more days.

Another surprise - I always had swollen knees for years. But now there's absolutely no swelling. Most of my inflammatory symptoms are completely gone now.

Also, before I took SuperWellness class, I had to be extremely strict about my eight hours of sleep. If I had one night with only six hours of sleep, all my flare-ups would come right back. But since SuperWellness, I do still make it a priority to sleep plenty, but I noticed that there are nights here or there where I only get two hours of sleep, and there is no pain or inflammation. Also my neck doesn't have any inflammation anymore either!

Here's another big surprise. After the course, I naturally turned raw vegan. It actually wasn't a decision, just from the juicing in the course, I noticed this nice feeling, like there's oxygen, a freshness, and coolness in my face and body that felt so good! It's like my pores were breathing and alive. So I just listened to that feeling. And whenever I see bread, or dairy, or many other things, they just don't appeal to me anymore.

It's all driven from inside. Now I tell everyone: *"Your body's gonna tell you what to do."* I did the prolonged juicing and never thought *"oh my god! I'm juicing!"* It all just happened naturally. It's what my body wanted. I felt the best juicing, but sometimes I just wanted to chew and eat with people. So gradually I ate different things. For three or four months after the SuperWellness class, I ate only raw vegan, not because I was trying, but because anything else I ate just didn't feel so good. So there are no rules, there is no protocol. I look at pork or beef, and it doesn't appeal to me. And I just listen to that now.

No willpower. No trying to tough it out. Just let your body tell you!

If you're tired, go to sleep! Breathe more, and everything just feels better. All my friends are asking me what I did, or how I did it. So I tell my friends what I learned. *"Listen to your body. Sleep more, and do things little by little. If you're going to try juicing, do the juices that taste good to you. There are no rules."* That's hard for people to understand sometimes.

Q: Wow! You said a lot of things there. Can we summarize some of the changes you experienced?

Marianne: First, all the inflammation is gone. I wasn't working because of my illness. Now I've gone back to work as a nurse. I can even handle 36 hours shifts now. I might still get a little bit puffy and bloated after the long shifts, but I come home and sleep 10 hours and feel completely fresh and recovered. Before SuperWellness, if ever there was one night of less than eight hours of sleep, I would have all my flare-ups.

Second, all my fibromyalgia symptoms are gone too. I have no fibromyalgia anymore.

The course was a big catalyst, because everything was introduced so gently and the timing was perfect. Something really clicked. We just introduced the juicing, and after a few days it was like *"Wow! I feel so much better!"* Plus we were all doing it together as a class, so I thought *"I'll keep going for a whole week."* It all happened naturally like that.

Third is that there are so many good things in the program, like backups and redundancies, so my sleep didn't have to always be 100% perfect. It's still important to sleep of course, but I'm not so delicate anymore. The breathing helps a lot. So many little things, like dealing with your stress, your emotions, your mood. Being grateful, being thankful, even when you're not feeling so well. It was not any one thing. There were so many things that all came together. But yeah, all the symptoms are pretty much gone now.

Q: What else did you learn about yourself?

Marianne: Well I feel I know now why I got so sick to begin with. I needed to clean up my body, and also my mind, emotions, and soul too. I can do many little things that really help. Right now, I'm happy to share all these little things with my patients too.

I also learned that it's not about willpower. With the juicing, I just liked the feeling of oxygen, being so light, so calm. I can really tell the difference when I'm eating crap vs. eating well now! You just choose to go with it. Not forcing it ever.

Q: Who is SuperWellness for? And who is it not for?

Marianne: Well I think EVERYONE should take it. I see my friends that are our age (in their 30's), and they're so busy, so stressed out. Some of them have kids, some of them are going through career changes. They go to the gym five days a week, but they eat horribly and are not sleeping, always running around and on the go. I try to tell them: *"Meditate. Learn to relax. Start with sleeping, and try some juicing, and experiment with your diet, listen to your body, and the rest will follow."* Just clear your mind, clear your stressful thoughts, and the rest follows naturally.

Honestly I think everyone should try SuperWellness, whether they're open-minded or not. I say just do it. I don't think there's anyone that this is not for! Even if they're not open-minded, if you just do the first week, it can change your life! Because you will interact with other people and see their experiences. It will be powerful. I just want you to give it a try, even just one week. Because you never know. Your heart will naturally open. There's nothing forced about it.

JOHN & MARIANNE'S STORY

Sharing the SuperWellness journey together as a family/couple.

Q: What can you share about your experience of doing SuperWellness together as a family, or as a couple?

John: I feel so grateful, because I knew a lot of data and research about the benefits of juicing, especially for Marianne's condition. So I tried to get Marianne to try juicing for a very, very long time! I used to make her juices in the morning and serve them to her. But she'd just look at it and say *"ew. that looks gross."*

Marianne: I know! (laughter) But now, since SuperWellness I really love to juice, because I associate it with this great feeling in my body.

John: I would say from my experience as a couple - if you're trying to help your partner get healthier, SuperWellness is a great program to do together. You can really support and help each other, because there are so many different things that you will learn together. And maybe you already know certain things, but now you can really practice it. Integrate it. The way it's presented, it's all very gentle. It works.

Marianne: It's all so organic, so natural. It's a very real experience, not like a class at all.

John: Yeah it doesn't feel like a class. Dr. Edith never comes across like a lot of those so-called "health gurus" out there, like: *"my way is the only way."* I think that's what opens things up for a lot of people.

Marianne: Yes. It feels like we're all in this together, and Dr. Edith is just sharing experiences, like we're all sitting in a living room, chatting and sharing. Very warm and open.

John: Yeah, there's never any authoritarian push or anything like that.

Marianne: So it was really good, because we do the practices together. John and I would share our experiences, how great it feels, and support each other. Like the time John told me he got pissed off after driving in bad traffic. Then he used the breathing and calmed down quickly. (laughter)

Q: How did SuperWellness influence the way you now support your friends and family?

Marianne: Well I used to always complain about my aches and pains. Then when I found the supplements and how much they helped, I would tell everybody to do the supplements too. Like "Step 1, do this. Step 2, do that."

John: Militant.

Marianne: Now It's more easy and natural, like we experienced in SuperWellness. It's not *"You must juice, you must eat this, you must take that supplement."* But it's more like *"It's up to you. Give it a try it. See what results you get, let your body tell you."* The more people see results, and it's not authoritarian, they will follow it naturally. Because it has to be natural. Otherwise it wouldn't last. If it's unnatural, it cannot be long-lasting.

John: Also for me, I felt SuperWellness provided the best foundation for anybody to kick start their health journey. I like being able to help people by just recommending them to SuperWellness as a great place to start.

Marianne: It's such a great community where you can share your feelings and experiences. Especially we women, we like to chat! (laughter) It was so great to see how you can create an environment where we share our feelings, but John also feels totally comfortable and never out-of-place in those conversations. It's such a great group of people. Great community.

MELISSA'S STORY

Single mom of three boys finds a simpler, kinder path to her self-care.

Melissa: My name is Melissa McGinn. I am 47 and a mother of three sons. I'm a San Francisco Bay Area native. I was married for 14 years. My husband died of cancer five years ago. Life changed drastically since then. It feels like I've had a totally different life since. That's the biggest thing about my background. I was a philosophy major in college and went on to graduate school in Library and Information Science, but I got married right around that time, so I never ended up working as a librarian.

Q: Please tell us why you chose to take the SuperWellness class?

Melissa: Well, I had seen the flyers for the class many times at the clinic throughout the years. It was always attractive to me because of my great experiences with Dr. Edith. But it was always difficult to coordinate with my schedule as a single mom with three kids. Finally, I decided to make it a priority because I was at a point where I really needed to make some changes to my health and explore what was in SuperWellness. I sensed that the class was very special and had great information and experiences that I wouldn't find anywhere else. Also I had some medications I was getting off of, I wanted to lose weight and just feel better. I wanted to improve my eating. It seemed like there are a lot of new and exciting ideas in SuperWellness that I couldn't find elsewhere. So that's what prompted me to take the class.

Q: What health challenges have you had in the past? What's worked, what's not worked for you?

Melissa: I've had challenges with my mood, energy, and weight. I gained some weight in my late 20s, probably 20-30 pounds that I wanted to lose. I tried various diet and workout programs over the years. Typically, I'd do super well in these programs for eight weeks. For some reason, eight weeks was kind of the drop off. I might lose ten pounds, but at eight weeks, things started to fall apart. Then I would have cravings, I'd slip back into old habits, not exercising, fall off the bandwagon. Then get back to it again a few months later. This process repeated many, many times. I had great success, but in short periods of time, nothing lasted.

In terms of my mood, that's a big piece for me. I have struggled with depression and anxiety and typically relied on antidepressants, but the side effects always end up bothering me. I did enjoy several years not being on them when I was doing acupuncture regularly. So I knew it was possible. That was a success that I wanted to get back to.

Q: Did you have any reservations or doubts about doing SuperWellness?

Melissa: No, I was excited and hopeful. But just the commitment made me a little nervous. I felt anxious leaving my three kids once a week and doing something new. But sometimes you just have to take the chance and jump in and do it.

Q: Tell us your experience in the SuperWellness class. Any surprises?

Melissa: It was such a great experience! I was so excited every week for our class. It was such a good group of people. That's one of the things that was surprising. I wasn't expecting to like everyone so much! Often in a group, some people try to dominate the conversation; there's always someone you wish they'd shut up. (laughter) That was never the case in this group at all! I really loved hearing from everyone. It was so great to know that every week I'd have these wonderful conversations with people that I enjoy so much and share our coursework together.

I definitely learned something new every week. A lot of the discoveries were profound. They really spoke to me. I was surprised that they were so deep, so profound, but also so simple and accessible. That was a big surprise - how easily accessible these great things are. They're right there for everybody.

Q: What kind of results did you experience?

Melissa: Well, I was able to taper down on my medications during SuperWellness, I think largely because of all the great lifestyle changes I was making. A month after the class, I was off all of my medications. I had been on three medications. I successfully tapered off all of them (with doctor's supervision of course). My eating improved tremendously. The F.A.N. diet was fantastic (pun not intended!). I lost seven pounds, which is as great as I've experienced in any program, but the huge difference is - this time it was effortless. It wasn't oppressive. I never felt deprived. Also, just my overall sense of energy and well-being increased as well.

(IMPORTANT: Melissa's medications were adjusted under careful supervision by her doctors. Do not ever change or discontinue any medication without the personal supervision of your doctors. SuperWellness does not diagnose, treat, or cure any medical condition, and it must never be used to replace any medical therapies.)

Q: What were some of your favorite tools or strategies from the course?

Melissa: One of my favorite tools is touching the earth every day. That one for me was huge, especially put in the context of why you feel so great when you're on vacation. You're so relaxed, and then you think it's because you're on vacation. But it's because you are doing all these great things. You're in the sunshine. You're walking barefoot on the earth at the beach. You're breathing. That to me is very calming. I love the grounding.

The sunlight and darkness - being exposed to light in the day, and then sleeping in darkness. I still use my sleep mask every morning. If I wake up at 4:00 a.m., I put it on so I sleep better for those last few hours. Those are my favorite tools. Plus the F.A.N. diet!

Q: What did you like about F.A.N. diet that's different from everything else out there?

Melissa: There's a lot more freedom! "Right and wrong" is determined by you. It's not like someone else giving you this plan that you can't follow because it's too strict or has things you don't like. It's for you to look in your heart and how you feel about food, what you enjoy. There's such an emphasis on what you enjoy. I mean, fun and tasty, that's #1! I found that very manageable to look at it food by food rather than a big prescription for what to eat, what not to eat.

One other thing that's a surprise was the juicing. That was scary to me going in. I didn't know how I was going to not eat for three days. But my experience was so remarkable! I had more energy. I was stunned to have more energy not eating anything. I had a new respect and awe of my body, what it was doing not eating solid foods. What the body's capable of and all the positive effects that came from that. It was so overwhelmingly positive; that was a surprise I didn't expect.

Q: How did that change your relationship with your body then?

Melissa: It made me realize that my body is a complex system, a product of evolution. It made me realize how much it's capable of and how different foods can affect it. That's an easy idea, but the fasting really made it hit home

- e.g. my skin improved so dramatically! To see the results, and to realize I'm eating these things that seem innocuous day to day, but somehow they're affecting me in this negative way... it gave me much more respect for my body.

Q: Who do you think SuperWellness is for, who is it not for?

Melissa: I would say it's for anyone who is interested in improving their health and well-being. I'd say it's not for people who want to "get ripped in 30 days" and want someone to tell them exactly what to do, i.e. here's what you must eat every day, here's how you exercise every day. It's not for people who want a superficial quick fix. It's not for people who aren't interested in learning new things.

But for anyone whom, when you hear that wellness is not just about "diet and exercise," if that idea sounds intriguing to you, then I'd say SuperWellness is for you!

Q: Final words of wisdom to our readers, especially those who are struggling to make healthy changes?

Melissa: Yes. I think SuperWellness gives you a chance to be kind to yourself when you're struggling because honestly, I'm struggling a little bit right now, but at the same time, I'm being kind to myself. In the past, if I'm having a hard time, I would make myself get on a strict diet and follow a strict exercise routine. Now, I remind myself to go outside, relax, get some sun, and get back to my gratitude journal, I know this turns into many other good things. It's a much kinder and easier way.

I think SuperWellness will open some doors you didn't even know were there. You have the answers inside of you. If you're open to a new process, new ideas, and finding out who you are on a deeper level, and what your body is capable of, then SuperWellness is for you.

VIKRAM'S STORY

An entrepreneur and lifelong "health-nut" discovers a huge treasure trove of new tools.

Vikram: My name is Vikram Kashyap. I'm an entrepreneur based in San Francisco.

Q: Why did you choose to take the SuperWellness class?

Vikram: I have a health condition that's of "unknown etiology" which basically means that they don't know the root cause, like with so many diseases. One of the greatest challenges I face is that doctors prescribe medications that don't address the root cause, nor do they fundamentally change the course of the disease. Many of these medications come with unwanted side effects. That's been quite a challenge for me, because the conventional treatment for my condition, inflammatory bowel disease, or ulcerative colitis, is not really very effective in my opinion. On top of this, I'm in a high-stress career that puts a lot of pressure on me, so it's challenging to maintain the level of health that I want to achieve. For many years, I've tried many different approaches to managing my health - from diet, to lifestyle, to drugs and medications, to alternative medicine to spirituality. I'm always interested to learn new things, so I wanted to take this class to see if I can learn something new.

Q: Did you have any reservations about SuperWellness? Any doubts in your mind?

Vikram: Well, I'm someone who reads and studies extensively on how to improve my health. For example, I read about nutrition every day just out of interest. So my biggest reservation about the class is whether or not I would learn anything new. Maybe it'd be the *"same old same old."* But Dr. Edith is so enthusiastic and passionate about her work, I wanted to give it a try.

Q: Tell us about your experience, any surprises?

Vikram: My experience with the program was extremely positive! I was introduced to a very different way of looking at my health, one that I had never considered before. The way health was framed in this entire course fundamentally shifted how I live my life to support my health now. More specifically, the course gave me some very practical tools that I could do daily, like ways to sleep, eat, breathe, ground, even the water I drink, etc., there were so many new things I learned!

Having been a long-time "health-nut", I was very surprised by how many new tools I learned. In fact, I would say the majority of the tools were new to me. Even the areas that I thought I already knew about, like nutrition and breathing, I was able to learn a fresh new approach during the course. I was very pleasantly surprised!

Q: How did the course shift your perspective on health?

Vikram: My greatest takeaway from SuperWellness is that "health" is not the absence of disease or an absence of symptoms. I believe the way our society thinks of symptoms and disease is what's feeding much of the unhealthiness that pervades in our world today. That old way of thinking about health was fundamentally challenged and shifted in this class.

The notion that you need to be proactive and be the CEO of your own health really resonated with me, because it's easy to fall back into the existing dogma of our healthcare system. It's not only in the world of conventional medicine, but even in alternative medicine too, the approach tends to be very "reactive." If you want real long-lasting health, you need to be proactive in your approach. This class gives the exact tools to do that.

Q: Please tell us some of your experience and results.

Vikram: Here's a specific example. I thought I knew a lot about Intermittent Fasting and things of that nature. But the way we experienced juicing and fasting in this course was something entirely different. It didn't have to be so strict, and there was more conscious intention behind the fasting. It helped me to understand that my strict reliance on certain types of food is not necessarily needed. I remember so clearly the day I broke my fast. The mindful eating. This idea of knowing and appreciating what you're eating. Slowing down, tasting everything. Savoring it. Enjoying it with gratitude.

It was an incredible and unforgettable experience.

Another great highlight is the Qigong practice, which I can use anytime when I'm low on energy. The notion that I'm not only dependent on my food for energy, but also through Qigong, grounding, sunlight, etc., those are the greatest takeaways for me.

Q: Who is SuperWellness for, and who is it not for?

Vikram: The truth is, anyone can benefit from SuperWellness! But I think this program is not for someone who's not ready to take control of their own health. If you have an open mind, if you're interested in learning new things, if you're open to testing things out and experimenting, then SuperWellness will empower you with invaluable tools!

Q: What advice do you have, or words of wisdom for our readers who are on the journey of healing, especially if they're feeling hopeless or frustrated?

Vikram: That there's hope! It's no secret to anyone that today's healthcare system in America is broken. In fact, I'd say if you're not frustrated with the healthcare system, you're in the minority. The good news is that if you take an ownership attitude with your health, then you can have an entirely different experience. Not only will you access better health, but your experience interacting with the healthcare system will be greatly improved too.

For anyone who feels hopeless and frustrated, you're not alone. You should read the book and take the SuperWellness classes, because there are a lot of easy things that you can do to empower yourself. Nowadays, it seems that everyone in the healthcare system is coming from different agendas. What I love about the agenda of SuperWellness is its mission to improve your health with free, simple, and proven tools. That's it! There's no ulterior motive of trying to sell you some expensive patented device or anything like that. The SuperWellness tools are simple, free, and they work!

LAURIE'S STORY

Finding a kinder, more loving approach to healthy living post-recovery from cancer treatments.

Q: Please tell us your name, a bit of your background, and why you chose to take the SuperWellness course?

Laurie: My name is Laurie Peterson. After the second time I got cancer, I needed to recover from the effects of chemo and began to see Dr. Edith for help. I always knew that healthy self-care is a critical piece on the journey of healing. Getting cancer the second time was a huge wakeup call. It meant business. It demanded change. Not just diet and exercise, but much more holistic changes. The problem is I struggled to make the lifestyle changes. I realized there were old patterns so deeply ingrained in me that, even with cancer twice, I still couldn't implement the changes I needed. I was stuck.

When I met Dr. Edith, she opened my eyes to a whole new way. She instilled in me this deeper awareness that made healthy living so much more simple, enjoyable and sustainable. So I decided to join the SuperWellness program.

Q: Did you have any reservations before taking the SuperWellness course?

Laurie: No reservations, except I always think twice before spending money. Now I know it was well worth every penny. The gifts of SuperWellness cannot possibly be measured. How can you put a price tag on this? It's not just for your health, but this deeper experience of life.

Q: What surprised you the most about SuperWellness?

Laurie: That it was all so easy, doable and sustainable! It never felt like more busy "to-dos" in my schedule. There's a new awareness about myself, and about life, that motivated me to implement the lifestyle tools and practices. It was all so enjoyable and doable!

Q: What were your biggest insights or takeaways from the program?

Laurie: My biggest realization was why all my previous attempts at healthy living never worked. They came from a cruel and judgmental place. Like a dictator in my mind. That's why they never worked. Also, I had long been interested in health. I read many books on diet, nutrition, and health. I would make these elaborate meal plans. Like most people, I was stuck in the rigid "Eat Right and Exercise" paradigm. On some level, I knew there had to be more to health. Now I understand why the "Diet and Exercise" paradigm felt so incomplete to me.

With SuperWellness, I have access to so many easy self-care tools. I can always access this state of well-being. And I don't have to be 100% perfect to get there. It's such a relief! I don't have to be so rigid with myself! This is a much kinder approach.

Q: Please tell us some of your results.

Laurie: Well, today I'm cancer free, and I honestly don't believe I could have made the necessary lifestyle changes without Dr. Edith and the SuperWellness program. When I went to my oncologist for a checkup recently, he was so impressed with how great I was doing. I had lost seven pounds (since implementing the SuperWellness lifestyle) and kept it off for the past 1.5 years without effort. It all happened naturally. My oncologist told me he sees patients yo-yo up and down in weight and lifestyle; they rarely sustain it. Cancer is a huge wakeup call, which motivates many people to follow a strict diet and exercise regimen. But then they fall off the bandwagon. So my oncologist was very impressed that I have found a sustainable way to stay healthy.

Since SuperWellness, I have a whole new reference point for the state of well-being that's possible. Well-being on all levels: mind, body, and spirit. It allowed many other positive changes and wonderful opportunities to come into my life.

Today, I'm so much more flexible, adaptive, and open to new possibilities. I no longer feel stuck. I know I can always learn, grow, and change at any age.

Q: Who is SuperWellness for? And who is it not for?

Laurie: It's not for Enlightened saints who are already levitating! (smiles) If you're already levitating and bi-locating, then maybe you don't need SuperWellness!

In all seriousness, SuperWellness is for EVERYBODY. I think we all need it. There's no one who wouldn't benefit.

Q: What advice or words of wisdom do you have for readers? Especially those who may be struggling with their health right now?

Laurie: Everyone gets called to approach their healing journey in a different way. Some people may do extreme dieting or other extreme therapies, but what if they are not sustainable? What then? We all need a way that gives us lifelong well-being, not just temporary short term results.

My #1 biggest takeaway from SuperWellness is this:

The only true lasting change comes from loving kindness towards yourself. That's what I learned from SuperWellness.

TIM'S STORY

Holistic wellness practitioner on the new multi-dimensional approach to health.

Tim: My name is Tim Asher, and I'm a Holistic Wellness Practitioner and an outdoors adventurer based in San Francisco.

Q: What made you decide to try the SuperWellness program?

Tim: Well, I knew Dr. Edith from being in the community and had done several programs she created in the past. They were always super fun, exciting and amazing cutting edge stuff! So I felt confident that SuperWellness would be excellent.

Q: Did you have any doubts or reservations before SuperWellness?

Tim: I've been a holistic wellness practitioner for a decade now, so I'm not exactly new to this world of self-care, self-healing and wellness. To be honest, I was skeptical as to whether or not I would really learn anything new. But Dr. Edith is super smart and so enthusiastic and fun to be around. I thought it would be a nice way to spend time deepening my understanding of wellness, with a group of wonderful and like-minded people. So that's why I decided to go for it.

Q: What was your experience like?

Tim: It was incredibly fun and informative! We always had great discussions. As a professional health practitioner, I gained priceless insights as I listened to the experiences of our classmates, who all came from very diverse backgrounds and were on different stages of their healing journeys. So as a professional health practitioner, I felt that being deeply immersed in this environment of inquiry and exploration greatly enhanced my patient-counseling skills. It went far beyond anything that we could learn in school.

Q: What was most surprising about the class?

Tim: Seeing the dramatic transformation of the participants! Wow. There wasn't a single person who didn't look and feel far brighter and more vibrant at the end of the course. But I was especially impressed by how quickly and dramatically the transformation took place for many of the people who were brand new to the world of wellness. Dr. Edith introduced to our group some very advanced ninja tricks that I only learned gradually over my ten years in this field. She has a gift of distilling things so elegantly. Everybody got to that highly advanced level within six weeks! It was like magic. I learned a lot from that.

Q: What was your favorite thing in the class?

Tim: My favorite thing was Byron Katie's "The Work." I must admit, at first I found it very challenging to confront the deeper levels of my stress and emotions. But as a health practitioner, time and time again I notice that the root of so many of my clients health issues are unresolved stresses, traumas, and emotions, which are difficult to access and heal in many cases. I feel that Byron Katie's tool cuts right to the core of most people's suffering. It's so powerful to have this simple framework for doing the deeper inner work. Today, this kind of inquiry has naturally integrated into my professional work, and it's been deeply transformative for all my clients.

Q: What was your biggest takeaway from the SuperWellness course?

Tim: True healing is much more than cleaning up our diet or exercising regularly. It's healing all the old wounds and prior stresses in our lives, to literally shed that old baggage so that we can go through life feeling light, happy and free. That's true healing. Through SuperWellness, I really came to appreciate that it doesn't have to be expensive or complicated to get to the core of our healing. We ALL have the capacity to heal.

Q: Tell us some of your specific results.

Tim: Personally, I was not struggling with any major health complaints, so I just felt lighter and brighter. But in terms of my professional wellness practice, I noticed a huge improvement in my lifestyle coaching skills! Because of the H.E.A.L.T.H. framework of SuperWellness, I had a new understanding of how to integrate and synthesize all the various self-care tools, most of which I had already learned from different places before. But for the first time, I understood how they could be woven together into a thoughtful and cohesive lifestyle program, delivering synergistic results that I never saw when the tools were used separately.

I also loved how SuperWellness is shared with so much joy and flexibility. I was able to make lifestyle tools more simple and approachable for my clients, which allowed people to take action right away and not get overwhelmed. As they saw the results, they naturally gravitated towards the next stage, and the next stage, and so on. So it became very easy to help my clients kick start their healing journey and get the best results.

Q: Who is SuperWellness for, and not for?

Tim: SuperWellness is for anyone who wants to be empowered to take their health into their own hands. It's not for people who just want a doctor to give them a magic pill for a temporary fix.

For health practitioners who want a more well-rounded and multi-dimensional approach to coaching their patients, one that honors all aspects - body, mind, emotions, and spirit - then SuperWellness is definitely for you!

Q: What advice or words of wisdom do you have for our readers?

Tim: Just take it one step at a time, don't worry about doing everything all at once, because the cards are stacked in your favor with this SuperWellness program. I believe if you only do 20% of the recommended tools and practices, it will already be a game-changer in your health. You can't go wrong. Just do one thing at a time!

LYNN'S STORY

Acupuncture practitioner on the deeper essence of healing, feeling 20% happier and 30-40% more confident!

Lynn: My name is Lynn Susan Belcher. I'm a Licensed Acupuncturist in California, and I also offer massage and bodywork. I've been in practice for 11 years now. I love what I do. I love being with my patients. It's such a nice and real connection with people.

Q: Tell us why you chose to take the SuperWellness course.

Lynn: Well, Dr. Edith is a total rock star! She has such great energy, and just knowing her for many years and seeing how passionate she was about putting SuperWellness together, I know it would be highly valuable information. Also, two years ago I took an entire year off to travel throughout South America to study and learn the true essence of healing. When I read the SuperWellness class discussion, it sounded like that's a huge part of SuperWellness too - the true essence of health and healing. I knew Dr. Edith was a very detail oriented person, and she would give me the real nuts and bolts that work. Plus, for Acupuncturists, the class is board approved for professional CEU credits. That was the icing on the cake!

Q: What are some challenges you've had with your own health, or when counseling your patients on their self-care?

Lynn: Well, for myself, it's sticking with something consistently. This is true for a lot of my patients too. We all get plenty of information, but how much are we really using and implementing? It's all about making these things part of our life and sticking to it.

For a lot of my patients, it's a feeling that *"Oh I can't do this, it's too big to take on."* Or *"There's not enough room in my life for this."* People get overwhelmed, and then it just doesn't happen. So it's really important to integrate the knowledge in bite-size chunks. Many patients know a lot. They have the information, but they don't know "how" to implement it.

I think we all want something that blends seamlessly into our lives, and not feel like it's this whole other big extra thing we have to do.

Q: Did you have any reservations before taking the SuperWellness course?

Lynn: No. I took the online course, so I didn't have to be at a certain place at a certain time. I just scheduled time in my calendar and completed every module. It was great!

Q: Please tell us about your experience. What were some big a-ha moments for you?

Lynn: I think the biggest takeaway for me is that I can change how I feel. If I'm feeling moody, or if I'm feeling tired, etc. I can make an action and quickly change my head-space. I can change my perspective, within two minutes. Instead of being mired by *"Oh I'm so tired…"* I have many tools to shift my energy now. The Qigong body pat down, oxygenating breaths every day, I do that every single day, without fail. It's an invaluable part of my life and I'm showing it to other people too.

Then there's this knowledge that - all I really need in order to feel better is free, plentiful and available most all the time. It's all here.

253

Another surprising discovery is learning about "how" we eat, vs. "what" we eat, and listening to how food makes us feel after we eat it. And I love this notion of programming the food, programming the water, structurizing our water, how I can bring my intention and supercharge my food and water with love, with energy, with good qualities. I can bring that into my body and let it do its work. So food is really a communion. I feel I can decide how I want my food to fuel me or feed me, whether it's French fries or chocolate cake, or carrots or kale! (laughter)

It's super fun. I'm a very visual person, so I have these elaborate energy practices, where I see myself in a web of connections. I am connected with my food.

I love the F.A.N. diet, just being reminded that if a food doesn't make us feel alive, it's not so good for our bodies. It was FANtastic! (laughter)

Q: How did SuperWellness influence the way you work with your patients?

Lynn: When I work with patients now, I've shifted to a "let's make this fun" strategy! I say: *"Why don't you give this a try? Have fun with it, let's experiment."* I love being able to say to my patients: *"You know your body better than anybody else. Try it, and then you decide."*

The fact that we're each our own best healthcare provider is a huge one. For me as a practitioner, I love that because when I make a suggestion for my patients, and they say *"Oh no, that doesn't work for me."* then I can be open and respond with *"Okay. You know yourself best. Then let's explore this."* Or, *"have you tried that?"* It creates a feeling of teamwork. It's very, very empowering.

Patients feel heard and respected. It's like: *"Oh, who me? Yeah I guess I do know something about my own health and my body!"* It helps me to instill in them a sense of personal responsibility, without even telling them this. It feels like we're equals, we're both healthcare practitioners sharing ideas. We both have the same goal in mind, so how can we do this together? Plus, the SuperWellness approach is just more fun! That's so important because who wants to do anything that's not fun or doesn't have good results?

Q: Speaking of results, what were some of your results? Or results that you've seen with patients from coaching them in this way?

Lynn: Well, for me I definitely feel more empowered about my own health and wellness; there's a greater awareness about all aspects of my habits. But to give specifics, I am consistently happier, because I do my oxygenating breaths and Qigong movements. I'm giving myself more time to rest. I make time to go see a sunrise. I take my shoes off on the earth. I just feel so much more connected, using all my own resources. So my entire sense of well-being is elevated.

For my patients, I think they see this new happiness and well-being in me, and it influences them in ways that maybe we're not even fully aware of. I share some of the tools from SuperWellness and my experience of being more proactive in taking advantage of these free and simple resources all around us. It's shifted a lot of my patients' perspectives.

If I were to put a number on it, I would say I feel 20% happier, and 30-40% more confident as a person.

Q: Confidence. Can you tell us more about the confidence?

Lynn: I'm confident in my ability to take care of myself, to feel well regardless of circumstances. And also to have fun! When I feel confident, I can let loose more, and have more fun. I know I can shift how my energy is in any situation. I am responsible for my own energy.

For example, I have this ongoing exchange with my mother, this dilemma between us - she wants me to spend a lot more time with her than I am. She'll text, get upset and say things like: *"Oh, I don't like your tone. You're objecting again."* So instead of reacting, I was able to feel it, be present with it. I took some breaths and did some of my Qigong movements, and got myself into a really clear, calm energy space, and I went outside and got grounded. Then, from that clear and grounded space, I wrote her back. It was just very loving, simple, clean. Not reactive.

Also at the clinic, when it's a long and busy day, I may have an intense conversation with one patient who is going through a hard time. Then the next patient is a new human being who's come in for a whole other situation. They deserve my full attention. I spend just two minutes in between to do some Qigong pat-down, breathing, drink my water, supercharger my water. And then it's all golden. I can be totally present.

When we start a session, that first moment - how I show up - sets the tone for that entire exchange. I'm aware that the patient looks at me, and they see me. My energy determines how the session will go. I'm aware that I can set the tone, or shift the tone of our exchange, through my presence and my energy.

Q: Wow. That's powerful. What would you say was your #1 biggest takeaway from SuperWellness, if you had to choose one?

Lynn: Before SuperWellness, I already knew that I'm responsible for my own energy. I'm responsible for everything that happens. But you know, you get tired, and it's easy to slip. But now I have a new appreciation of how easy and available the tools are to change my energy at any moment.

So my biggest takeaway is that the tools are all around us. It's free. It's available!

It's really exciting to be able to share with my patients that what we need to be healthy, energized, and happy, is so simple. It's right here. But I don't just tell people, I do the work.

Q: Who do you think SuperWellness is for? Who is not for?

Lynn: It's definitely for health practitioners, because we all know these things, but the way that Dr. Edith weaves the science together with the activities, the way that we experience the journey, tapping into our emotions and feelings… the course gets all our senses involved. So you really get it. It's very inspiring and invigorating.

I think most practitioners could use some inspiration and re-invigoration!

Also, new ways to talk with our patients. I love that I can always go back through the video course to revisit the nuggets and have so much exciting new information to chat about with my patients.

For patients/people who feel bogged down, overwhelmed, struggling - anyone who feels frustrated with our medical system because it's not working for them, SuperWellness is a great resource.

Honestly I think it's for everybody. Old people, young people. I wish I took this course when I was 17 years old! Wow. If I could have started my adult life with this kind of awareness, everything would have been magnified so much by now.

Who is it not for? People who are super closed-minded and think they know everything. It's probably not for them. But... it could still be good for them! Because Dr. Edith never says "this is the way it is." She always encourages people to try things out and experiment and decide for themselves. So that's huge. This course weaves together such simple truths - sunshine, touching the earth, breathing, water. It just resonates.

I think SuperWellness is especially powerful for people living in urban environments. Because there's not a lot of nature around us. So it helps us to take maximum advantage of the nature that we can get, to look for those things. It's so easy to forget that we need it, when we don't have much green space in the city.

Q: Final words of wisdom or advice for our readers?

Lynn: Incorporate SuperWellness tools into what you're already doing. It doesn't have to be some separate extra thing!

For example, instead of Gratitude journals, I do gratitude walks or gratitude bike rides. I do my ten minute bike ride commuting to work. So my routine is to focus on my breathing during the first half. Then the second half is gratitude bicycling. I look around and think about all the things I'm thankful for when I'm pedaling. It's my daily Gratitude bicycling! I would have never done that before SuperWellness. But by the time I get to work, I feel "Everything is great!" and it's so much fun!

You can be washing the dishes and breathing. It doesn't have to be complicated!

Other words of wisdom? The body is designed to be healthy and strong, and what we need to feel happy and energized is available, free, and abundant. If what you're doing is not working, then trust that there's a better way somewhere else. Keep looking. Find out what that is.

Also, focus on how you eat, this conscious communion with food. It's a very intimate thing to be able to share this biochemical and physical exchange with another organism. The food gets inside us and perfuses all throughout our being. So it's not something to just shove down your throat. I think we don't need to go to church to have a sacred experience. Just sit down and eat a tomato or something! When you slow down, in the state of gratitude and appreciation, you can become aware of the profound sacredness of that experience.

The more we love ourselves, the more we become aware of these things, and the better we take care of ourselves. It all happens naturally. It's beautiful.

Wow. Powerful words of wisdom from our fellow SuperWellness heroes! I love that they shared such diverse perspectives, but there are common threads of kindness, love, joy, and freedom that can be felt in each story. After reading their inspirational words, I hope you feel even more excited and empowered to start implementing SuperWellness into your life, in your own perfect way. We look forward to hearing your success story and your words of wisdom in the online forum!

In our next and final chapter, let's ensure that you have the best possible experience on your SuperWellness journey with important guidelines for "Dos and Don'ts."

CHAPTER 11

Tips for Success - Dos and Don'ts

"Mind what you have learned. Save you it can."

~ Yoda ~

B esides the words of wisdom from our SuperWellness heroes in Chapter 10, below are some dos and don'ts inspired by commonly asked questions that I've received over the years from our SuperWellness community.

SuperWellness opens us up to a wonderful new world of possibilities. There are so many layers of goodness in the SuperWellness program that we really can't "lose", i.e. the cards are stacked in your favor! Still, it is a big transition from the old paradigm. So to ensure the best possible experience, I encourage you to keep these dos and don'ts in mind.

DON'T	DO
Don't over-complicate your self-care regimen. Don't try to implement all of H.E.A.L.T.H. right from the get-go. Take your time to establish the practices in H first. Then E, then A, and so on. Add them gradually over time. This is a lifelong practice.	**Do** keep things simple. If you just commit to daily breathing and gratitude practice, that is already a phenomenal beginning. Do allow the results to surprise you!

Don't let your health happen by accident. Let's be honest, if it's not on the calendar, if you don't block time for your self-care, it's unlikely it will happen. The outside world is constantly pulling us into distraction and noise. There's always something going on, isn't there? Let's make <u>you</u> the priority. You deserve it!	**Do** schedule your SuperWellness practices into your calendar. Block the time, and make your self-care a priority. You are the architect of your life and your schedule. You get to design your day in the way that works for you!
Don't overly obsess about metrics or results that you have no immediate control over. (e.g. *"I must weigh exactly X lbs/kg by X date."*) The results will happen as a natural side-effect of taking great care of yourself.	**Do** focus on cultivating your practices. Set goals that emphasize factors within your control. What can you do each and every day to enhance your well-being? (e.g. *"I will commit to a 8-10min breathing practice every day."*) Let the results happen as a side-effect.
Don't be too harsh on yourself. There's no such thing as a wrong way to live, and no such thing as perfection either!	**Do** something every day that is kind and loving for yourself. Do look for and see the perfection in every moment.
Don't get trapped into old thinking that complicated, fancy, or expensive is necessarily better. Without a solid foundation first, the "house" of your well-being would be built on shaky ground.	**Do** commit to cultivating your simple foundational practices. The world's highest achievers in sports and business alike are superb at mastering the basics consistently. If we want superb health, let's master the basics.
Don't align your health and wellness practices around the fear of disease.	**Do** align your health and wellness practices around your <u>love for life</u>!

Don't feel you have to be a loner on your journey of healing. Social learning and community support is the key to success!	**Do** find community (local and online). Share your new SuperWellness lifestyle with friends and family! Do join our SuperWellness online forum and share your experiences with us. We can't wait to hear from you!
Don't force your opinions onto friends and family. Allow space for everyone to find their own path.	**Do** focus on your own self-care and inner work. If friends and family ask you, be generous in sharing your excitement and experiences, without pressuring others to do things exactly your way.
Don't run away from your negative thoughts and emotions. Don't try to suppress or ignore your stressful thoughts. We cannot fake our happiness. Genuine happiness comes from embracing all the ups and downs of life.	**Do** embrace your fears, sadness, and emotions as opportunity to practice unconditional love for yourself. Make friends with your stressful thoughts and use a process like "The Work" to understand your mind more deeply.
Don't let limited thinking trap you into the mindset of a victim for too long, especially beware during moments of illness or injury or fatigue.	**Do** remember that you are a vast and infinite being. You are the master and CEO of your life. You are smart, creative, and resourceful. You can always find a way.
Don't become overly obsessed about what you cannot do during moments of illness or injury. Because even if you have limitations, there's always much you can still do. You are alive and breathing. Be loving to yourself and find joy in what you can do.	**Do** find creative ways to modify your activities during moments of illness or injuries, so that you do not overly limit yourself. Continue to cultivate a holistic way of life that you love! Do what you can do, and celebrate life!

Don't hesitate to reach out for support amongst friends, family, and community.	**Do** stay connected with us and share your experiences with our global SuperWellness community!
Don't undervalue our good-hearted doctors just because there are some issues with the old "sick"care system. Every doctor I know is working hard and doing their best with an imperfect system. Their advanced training is here to save lives. All the doctors I know have the very best intention to serve. Much respect to our doctors!	**Do** seek help from professional practitioners and get appropriate support, especially for symptoms or conditions that requires diagnosis and treatment. Remember that SuperWellness is not a substitute for professional medical advice; it does not diagnose or treat any medical conditions.
Don't get sucked into any diet, workout, or lifestyle systems that don't feel right for you. No more dogma. No more rigid and militant programs that take all the fun and joy out of life.	**Do** listen to your body when it comes to any of your self-care or lifestyle practices. Do what is safe, gentle and loving. Do test things out and decide what works for you. Throw away what doesn't work for you.
Don't just read this book once. Don't miss out on the interactive exercises and "SuperWellness Labs." It is only with implementation that we can experience the true gifts of SuperWellness.	**Do** read this book multiple times, and take your time to implement at your own perfect pace. Do log-on to your book bonuses regularly, which will stay updated with the latest cutting edge information.
Don't just get one copy of this book and keep all these SuperWellness treasures to yourself. Good things are for sharing!	**Do** buy many more copies and gift to all your friends, family, and health practitioners! Everyone deserves to enjoy a joyful, healthy and fulfilling life!

THE OLD "SICK"CARE SYSTEM VS. THE NE WORLD OF SUPERWELLNESS

Surely this book will inspire <u>many</u> fascinating and thought-provoking conversations amongst your friends, family, and community. Your friends may ask questions like: *"How is SuperWellness new or different?"* or *"What's so awesome about it?"* So I've created a great resource for you as a conversation starter.

Below are the key differences between the Old Paradigm of "Sick"care vs. this New Paradigm of SuperWellness. What do you think? What else might you add to this? Please share with us in our online forum. As a SuperWellness community, let's collaborate and enhance our body of knowledge together. I look forward to hearing from you!

The "Sick"care System	SuperWellness
Health takes sacrifice and willpower.	Health is fun and requires zero deprivation.
The "system" will take care of us.	We're in charge of our own health.
The best health care is expensive.	Many best healing strategies are free and easily accessible.
Your body cannot heal without drugs or surgery.	Your body is designed to heal naturally.
Genes determine your health, and they're fixed.	We can influence our genes through environment, lifestyle, and conscious living.

"There's no cure for your condition." or "There's nothing you can do about it."	There's a vast world of alternatives beyond drugs and surgery.
The body, mind, emotions, and spirit are all separate. They are addressed separately. Some conditions are all in your head. Some are only in your body.	The body-mind-emotions-soul complex is an integrated system that thrives with a holistic approach.
Health is the absence of detectable illness/disease.	Health is our capacity to adapt to life's stressors, and learn and grow from every experience.

THE SUPERWELLNESS MANIFESTO

SUPERWELLNESS IS OUR BIRTHRIGHT. IT'S OUR NATURAL STATE. We've outgrown the old "sick"care system. It's time to take back control of our Health. The truth about our health is far more empowering than we've been told. As we heal ourselves, we change the world. This is the healthcare reform we've all been waiting for. **TRUE VIBRANT HEALTH IS FUN, JOYFUL, AND REQUIRES ZERO DEPRIVATION!** The best healing tools are often simple, free, and abundantly available. It's up to each of us to take beautiful care of ourselves and our well-being. **ERADICATE STRESS. B-R-E-A-T-H-E. MASTER OUR ENERGY. CREATE A LIFE WE LOVE!** Movement. Stillness. Community. Hugs. Laughter. Joy. Touch the Earth. Embrace Sunlight during the day and Darkness at night. Let's live in harmony with Nature again. **SLOW DOWN. ENJOY LIFE. LIGHTEN UP. PURIFY. SIMPLIFY**. Food should be Fun! Bye-bye to fad diets. HOW we Eat is even more important than WHAT we Eat. Our bodies are designed to heal. Health is not the absence of illness or disease, but the capacity to adapt, learn, and grow from every experience. **WE DESERVE TO FEEL WHOLE.** We deserve wellness on all levels - body - mind - emotions - soul. SuperWellness is the most LOVING gift I can give to myself, my family, and my community. Becoming healthy & whole is powerful social activism. **SuperWellness is WELLNESS FOR THE NEW HUMANITY.**

JOIN THE MOVEMENT – SUPERWELLNESS.COM

ACKNOWLEDGEMENT

"Ubuntu" means *"I am what I am, because of what we all are."*

The birth of this book would not have been possible without the support of a village of angels. This book is the embodiment of Ubuntu. *"This book is what it is, because of what we all are."*

Without a doubt, the #1 angel that deserves my deepest gratitude in this project is Stephan Wilmas of Keya Digital. At every step of the journey, he went above and beyond the call of duty - from cover design to interior layout, from editing to cheerleading, to the creation of our website - he did it all! Being the light warrior that he is, Stephan "machete'ed" through every obstacle with grace, ease, and joy. He poured his heart and soul into every last detail to ensure its greatest success. Words cannot describe my gratitude!

To my husband David and magical wonder boy Kabreem, who nourished me throughout this project with never-ending love, hugs, jokes and laughter whenever I got too serious for my own good.

To my dear friend Wim Hof - thank you for blessing this project with your special foreword. More importantly, thank you for devoting your life to awakening our greatest human possibilities. Your heart, soul, and being-ness inspires me and everybody with whom you meet. Thank you for being you!

To my mentors Mas Sajady and Brendon Burchard, whose powerful coaching and business masterminds gave me the courage, alignment, and practical tools to serve our world at the highest levels.

To my soul-brother Noam Salpeter, who first introduced me to Wim Hof, and was instrumental in the final editing of this book. Noam, you are such a treasure. My gratitude for the gift of our friendship is beyond description.

Thanks to SuperWellness heroes – Lisa Pezik, Marianne Torres, John Chavez, Zahra Kassam, Melissa McGinn, Lynn Belcher, Vikram Kashyap, Laurie Peterson, and Tim Asher – for their inspiring and powerful testimonials in Part III of this book.

To my book coaches Allan Ting and Venessa Moss, whose never-ending patience, expertise, and cheerleading was instrumental to the birth of this book.

A special shout out to our dear friend Yun Suh, longtime SuperWellness grad, who originated the idea of the "H.E.A.L.T.H." framework, and to my husband David who came up with "Agua & Aaaarmph!"

Huge thanks also to Shannon O'Sullivan, our superstar office manager at Dan Tian Wellness, who always gives her very best self to every task at hand. Thank you for rising above and beyond the call of duty, assisting with many mission-critical steps along the journey of this book. You made it all possible!

To Nicolai Crane and Michael Axtell, thank you for all the love you poured into our Video Book Bonuses. This book would not be the groundbreaking project that it is without your special video magic. Thank you!

Gratitude to my world-class personal trainer and friend Charlie Reid, who kept me healthy, vibrant, and strong. Charlie inspired much of the insights and humor that was found in this book. If you didn't love the kale smoothie joke, you can blame Charlie.

Heartfelt thanks to all our Dan Tian Wellness interns, patients, and SuperWellness students for your never-ending support. You're the true midwives of the SuperWellness movement!

Gratitude to my astrologer Michelle Karen, who gave this book its special blessing from the stars. To my dearest friends Rich and Dida Merrill - thank you for always accompanying me and cheering me to grow, learn, and evolve as a multi-dimensional being on this precious earth journey.

Thanks to our amazing babysitters Fiona, Kandis, Paulette, who brought much needed spaciousness, order, and sanity into our sometimes chaotic toddler-run household so that this book could be born.

To my extended family, especially my sister, my parents, my aunts and uncles. Thank you for supporting me so unconditionally throughout the years. I'm sorry to have caused such worry when I left software to become a "starving grad student!" Thanks for all your generous "red pocket money" that made it possible for me to pursue my dreams! Most of all, thank you for loving me despite all my quirky and unconventional ways.

Special love and gratitude for my sister Belinda and my ma Susan, who show me how to rise to challenges and never shy away from hard work, dedication, and attention to detail, when the situation calls for it.

Thanks to Mahlon and Gene, for giving me the best husband ever, and for always loving and supporting David, Kabreem, and me.

To all my teachers, mentors, friends, and community along the journey of life - from Fay School to Philips Exeter Academy to Harvard University, to American College of Traditional Chinese Medicine, Five Branches University, and all my "oldskool" San Francisco Triathlon Club friends. You have all influenced and inspired me in powerful ways that are beyond description. A special dedication to the memory of Jacqueline Stolte, whose spirit continues to bless me at every important juncture of this precious life.

Finally and most importantly, to my teacher Dr. Fu, who accepted me as Chinese Medicine apprentice with such open-arms and loving kindness. (and to my apprenticeship brother Ben Krieg, L.Ac..) Thank you for guiding me into the deepest mysteries, beauty, and wonder of Chinese Medicine, far beyond anything that could be shared in a textbook. Not a day goes by, where I do not draw great inspiration from your teachings. Your timeless wisdom (and humor!) has enriched every aspect of my life and made me into the practitioner that I am today. 永遠的感谢您,傅大夫!

ABOUT THE AUTHOR

Dr. Edith Ubuntu Chan is a Holistic Chinese Medicine Doctor, author, speaker, and coach who has devoted her life to unlocking the secrets of our human potential. She shares a refreshingly new approach to wellness that integrates science, medicine, and spirituality. Her story began in 2003 with a series of meditation-induced mystical experiences, which gave Dr. Edith extraordinary insights into our human possibilities. She believes that health is our birthright. It's our natural state.

Dr. Edith has been featured on CNN, Yoga Journal, Lilou Macé's Juicy Living Tour, "The Goddess Project" documentary and more. Her academic background includes a Doctoral Degree from Five Branches University in Endocrinology & Neuromuscular Medicine, a graduate degree from American College of Traditional Chinese Medicine, and a Bachelors with Magna Cum Laude in Applied Mathematics from Harvard University.

Through her seminars and programs, Dr. Edith helps Visionary Pioneers become masters of their energy, alignment, and joy, so that they can lead and serve at the highest levels. Weaving together ancient wisdom and modern science, SuperWellness is a powerful and practical distillation of her entire life's work. Meet Dr. Edith at: www.DrEdithUbuntu.com.

REFERENCES

Introduction

[1] Alonso-Zaldivar. "New Peak for US Health care spending: $10,345 per person." *Associated Press*, July 13, 2016.
https://apnews.com/dd6612ead1a14cd39bcca0be8758ef79/new-peak-us-health-care-spending-10345-person

[2] Rubenstein, Grace. "New Health Rankings: Of 17 Nations, U.S. Is Dead Last." *The Atlantic*, January 10, 2013.
https://www.theatlantic.com/health/archive/2013/01/new-health-rankings-of-17-nations-us-is-dead-last/267045/

Chapter 1

[3] Cormier, Jordyn. "Stress Reduction is More Important Than Eating Well." *Care2*, October 3, 2016. http://www.care2.com/greenliving/stress-reduction-is-more-important-than-eating-well.html

[4] Kiecolt-Glaser, J.K., et al. "Depression, Daily Stressors and Inflammatory Responses to High-Fat Meals: When Stress Overrides Healthier Food Choices." *Molecular Psychiatry*. Macmillan Publishers Limited, 2017.
https://www.nature.com/articles/mp2016149.epdf

[5] Anson, Pat. "Study Claims 10% of Pain Patients Addicted to Opioids." *Pain News Network*, March 31, 2015.
https://www.painnewsnetwork.org/stories/2015/3/31/study-claims-10-of-pain-patients-addicted-to-opioids

[6] "Addiction." *YouTube*. Kurzgesagt - In a Nutshell, October 29, 2015.
https://www.youtube.com/watch?v=ao8L-0nSYzg

Chapter 2

[7] Colino, Stacey. "How Much Do Doctors Learn About Nutrition?" *U.S. News*, December 7, 2016. https://health.usnews.com/wellness/food/articles/2016-12-07/how-much-do-doctors-learn-about-nutrition

[8] Rani Polak, MD, MBA, Rachele M. Pojednic, PhD, EdM, MS, and Edward M. Phillips, MD, "Lifestyle Medicine Education" *American Journal of Lifestyle Medicine*. Sept 2015. https://www.ncbi.nlm.nih.gov/pmc/articles/PMC4561845/

[9] "A Super Brief and Basic Explanation of Epigenetics for Total Beginners." *What Is Epigenetics*, July 30, 2013. https://www.whatisepigenetics.com/what-is-epigenetics/

[10] Alonso-Zaldivar. "New Peak for US Health care spending: $10,345 per person." *Associated Press,* July 13, 2016. https://apnews.com/dd6612ead1a14cd39bcca0be8758ef79/new-peak-us-health-care-spending-10345-person

[11] Rubenstein, Grace. "New Health Rankings: Of 17 Nations, U.S. Is Dead Last." *The Atlantic*, January 10, 2013. https://www.theatlantic.com/health/archive/2013/01/new-health-rankings-of-17-nations-us-is-dead-last/267045/

Chapter 3

[12] "Beyond McMindfulness." *Huffington Post*, July 1, 2013. https://www.huffingtonpost.com/ron-purser/beyond-mcmindfulness_b_3519289.html

[13] Brandon, John. "The Surprising Reason Millennials Check Their Phones 150 Times a Day." *Inc.*, April 17, 2017. https://www.inc.com/john-brandon/science-says-this-is-the-reason-millennials-check-their-phones-150-times-per-day.html

[14] Medical FAQ. "Average lung capacity answers." http://www.medicalfaq.net/average_lung_capacity/ta-23948

[15] Bradford, Alina. "Lungs: Facts, Function and Diseases." *Live Science*, September 21, 2015.

https://www.livescience.com/52250-lung.html

[16] Bradford, Alina. "Lungs: Facts, Function and Diseases." *Live Science*, September 21, 2015.
https://www.livescience.com/52250-lung.html

[17] Seppala, Emma. "Benefits of Breathing: The Scientific Benefits of Breathing Infographic." *Emma Seppala*, February 7, 2014.
https://emmaseppala.com/benefits-breathing-scientific-benefits-breathing-infographic/

[18] Herrington, Diana. "13 Health Benefits of Deep Breathing." *Care2*, May 22, 2013. http://www.care2.com/greenliving/13-health-benefits-of-deep-breathing.html

[19] Kox, M., et al. "Voluntary Activation of the Sympathetic Nervous System and Attenuation of the Innate Immune Response in Humans." *US National Library of Medicine National Institutes of Health*, May 5, 2014.
https://www.ncbi.nlm.nih.gov/pubmed/24799686

[20] McCullough, Michael E. "The New Science of Gratitude." *Gratitude Power*, 2013. http://gratitudepower.net/science.htm

[21] A Network for Grateful Living, 2017. https://gratefulness.org/

Chapter 4

[22] "Disorder and Treatments: Insomnia." *Sleep Management Institute*, 2010.
http://www.sleepmanagement.md/sleepdisorders/Insomnia.aspx

[23] Sparacino, Alyssa. "11 Surprising Health Benefits of Sleep." *Health*. Health Media Ventures, July 21, 2013.
http://www.health.com/health/gallery/0,,20459221,00.html#go-ahead-snooze--1

[24] Klein, Sarah. "8 Ways Working The Night Shift Hurts Your Health." *Huffington Post*, August 14, 2014.
https://www.huffingtonpost.com/2014/08/14/shift-work-health-risks_n_5672965.html

[25] Whitaker, Julian. "Beyond Sleep: Other Benefits of Melatonin." *Dr. Whitaker*, 2017. https://www.drwhitaker.com/beyond-sleep-other-benefits-of-melatonin

[26] "Melatonin." *Life Extension Magazine*, June 2007. http://www.lifeextension.com/magazine/2007/6/nu_melatonin/Page-01

[27] Cohen, Joseph. "24 Surprising Health Benefits of Melatonin – Sleep, Brain, Gut Health, Antiaging, Cancer, Fertility." *Self Hacked*, October 11, 2017. https://selfhacked.com/blog/melatonin/

[28] "Living & Coping With Shift Work Disorder." *National Sleep Foundation*, 2017. https://sleepfoundation.org/shift-work/content/living-coping-shift-work-disorder

[29] Scutti, Susan. "7 Health Consequences of Going to Bed Past Midnight." *Medical Daily*, June 28, 2013. http://www.medicaldaily.com/7-health-consequences-going-bed-past-midnight-247247

[30] "What Is Vitamin D?" *Vitamin D Council*, 2017. https://www.vitamindcouncil.org/about-vitamin-d/what-is-vitamin-d/

[31] Frellick, Marcia. "Avoiding Sun as Dangerous as Smoking." *Medscape*, March 23, 2016. https://www.medscape.com/viewarticle/860805

[32] Lindqvist, P.G., et al. "Avoidance of Sun Exposure is a Risk Factor for All-Cause Mortality: Results from the Melanoma in Southern Sweden Cohort." *US National Library of Medicine National Institutes of Health*, April 23, 2014. https://www.ncbi.nlm.nih.gov/pubmed/24697969

[33] Ainsleigh, H.G. "Beneficial Effects of Sun Exposure on Cancer Mortality." *US National Library of Medicine National Institutes of Health*, January 22, 1993. https://www.ncbi.nlm.nih.gov/pubmed/8475009

[34] Hoel, David G., et al. "The Risks and Benefits of Sun Exposure 2016." *US National Library of Medicine National Institutes of Health*, October 19, 2016. https://www.ncbi.nlm.nih.gov/pmc/articles/PMC5129901/

[35] Praschak-Rieder, Nicole. "Treatment of Seasonal Affective Disorders." *US National Library of Medicine National Institutes of Health*, December 2003. https://www.ncbi.nlm.nih.gov/pmc/articles/PMC3181778/

[36] "Phototherapy." *National Psoriasis Foundation*, 2017. https://www.psoriasis.org/about-psoriasis/treatments/phototherapy

[37] Dai, Tianhong, et al. "Ultraviolet C Irradiation: An Alternative Antimicrobial Approach to Localized Infections?" *US National Library of Medicine National Institutes of Health*, December 1, 2012. https://www.ncbi.nlm.nih.gov/pmc/articles/PMC3292282/

[38] "Lack of Interest in Sex Successfully Treated by Exposure to Bright Light." *Science Daily*, September 18, 2016. https://www.sciencedaily.com/releases/2016/09/160918214443.htm

[39] Quirk, B.J., et al. "Effect of Near-Infrared Light on In Vitro Cellular ATP Production of Osteoblasts and Fibroblasts and on Fracture Healing with Intramedullary Fixation." *US National Library of Medicine National Institutes of Health*, March 10, 2016. https://www.ncbi.nlm.nih.gov/pubmed/27857496

[40] "UV Exposure Directly Lowers Blood Pressure." *Vitamin D Council*, May 8, 2013. https://www.vitamindcouncil.org/uv-exposure-directly-lowers-blood-pressure/

[41] "LED Device Illuminates New Path to Healing." *NASA*. https://spinoff.nasa.gov/Spinoff2008/hm_3.html

[42] Sawyer, Taylor L. "Phototherapy for Jaundice." *Medscape*, December 6, 2015. https://emedicine.medscape.com/article/1894477-overview

[43] Silver, Val. "Healing with Light and Color Therapy." *Val Silver's Holistic Mindbody Healing*. Val Silver, 2017. http://www.holistic-mindbody-healing.com/healing-with-light.html

[44] Mercola, Joseph. "How LED Lighting May Compromise Your Health." *Mercola*, October 23, 2016. https://articles.mercola.com/sites/articles/archive/2016/10/23/near-infrared-led-lighting.aspx

[45] Paul, Marla. "Bright Light Alters Metabolism." *Northwestern*, May 18, 2016. https://news.northwestern.edu/stories/2016/05/bright-light-alters-metabolism/

[46] Zucker, Marty, et al. "The Healing Benefits of Grounding the Human Body." *Huffington Post*, May 29, 2017. https://www.huffingtonpost.com/entry/the-healing-benefits-of-grounding-the-human-body_us_592c585be4b07d848fdc058a

[47] Snyder, Kimberly. "The Invisible Benefits of Grounding." *Kimberly Snyder*, January 16, 2014. https://kimberlysnyder.com/blog/2014/01/16/invisible-benefits-grounding/

[48] Sinatra, Stephen. "Grounding/Earthing." *YouTube*. Dr. Sinatra's Heart MD Institute, April 20, 2010. https://www.youtube.com/watch?v=XumPQLTzPWI

Chapter 5

[49] "Tapped Out?: Are Chlorine's Beneficial Effects in Drinking Water Offset by Its Links to Cancer?" *Scientific American*, 2017. https://www.scientificamerican.com/article/earth-talks-tapped-out/

[50] "Countries That Fluoridate Their Water." *Fluoride Action Network*, August 2012. http://fluoridealert.org/content/bfs-2012/

[51] Connett, Paul. "50 Reasons to Oppose Fluoridation." *Fluoride Action Network*, September 2012. http://fluoridealert.org/articles/50-reasons/

[52] Donn, Jeff, et al. "Pharmawater I: Pharmaceuticals Found in Drinking Water, Affecting Wildlife and Maybe Humans." *The AP National Investigation*. http://hosted.ap.org/specials/interactives/pharmawater_site/day1_01.html

[53] Fallik, Dawn. "This New Study Found More Drugs in Our Drinking Water Than Anybody Knew." *New Republic*, December 10, 2013. https://newrepublic.com/article/115883/drugs-drinking-water-new-epa-study-finds-more-we-knew

[54] Lui, Kevin. "Plastic Fibers Are Found in 83% of the World's Tap Water, a New Study Reveals." *Time Inc.*, September 6, 2017. http://time.com/4928759/plastic-fiber-tap-water-study/

[55] Andrews, David. "'Erin Brockovich' Carcinogen in Tap Water of More Than 200 Million Americans." *Environmental Working Group*, September 20, 2016. https://www.ewg.org/research/chromium-six-found-in-us-tap-water#.WhmixBNSyRs

[56] Cohen, Joseph. "Interview With Dr. Gerald Pollack: Using Water For Optimal Health." *Self Hacked*, October 11, 2017.

https://selfhacked.com/blog/interview-with-dr-gerald-pollack-using-water-for-optimal-health/

[57] Skerrett, Patrick J. "Crumbling, Confusing Food Pyramid Replaced by a Plate." *Harvard Health Publishing*, June 3, 2011 (updated January 28, 2016). https://www.health.harvard.edu/blog/crumbling-confusing-food-pyramid-replaced-by-a-plate-201106032767

[58] Campbell, Joseph. "12 Frightening Facts About Milk." *Center for Nutrition Studies*, October 31, 2014. http://nutritionstudies.org/12-frightening-facts-milk/

[59] Phillip, Abby. "Study: Milk May Not Be Very Good for Bones or the Body." *The Washington Post*, October 31, 2014. https://www.washingtonpost.com/news/to-your-health/wp/2014/10/31/study-milk-may-not-be-very-good-for-bones-or-the-body/?utm_term=.a2a02856be78

[60] Mercola, Joseph. "What Happens to Your Body When You Eat Too Much Sugar?" *Mercola*. Dr. Joseph Mercola. https://articles.mercola.com/sugar-side-effects.aspx

Chapter 6

[61] Chung, Tsai Chih, Bruya, Brian. *Zen Speaks: Shouts of Nothingness*, Princeton University Press, 1994.

[62] Hanh, Thich Nhat. *Anger*. Riverhead Books, 2002.

[63] Albers, Susan. "The Surprising Benefits of Mindful Eating." *Huffington Post*, February 13, 2012 (updated April 14, 2012). https://www.huffingtonpost.com/dr-susan-albers/mindful-eating_b_1265865.html

[64] Reis de Azevedo, Fernanda, et al. "Effects of intermittent fasting on metabolism in men." *Science Direct*, March 31, 2013. http://www.sciencedirect.com/science/article/pii/S0104423013000213

[65] Heilbronn, Leonie K., et al. "Alternate-Day Fasting in Nonobese Subjects: Effects on Body Weight, Body Composition, and Energy Metabolism." *The American Journal of Clinical Nutrition*, January 2005. http://ajcn.nutrition.org/content/81/1/69.short

[66] Varady, Krista A., et al. "Short-Term Modified Alternate-Day Fasting: a Novel Dietary Strategy for Weight Loss and Cardioprotection in Obese Adults." *The American Journal of Clinical Nutrition,* September 30, 2009. http://ajcn.nutrition.org/content/90/5/1138

[67] Antoni, Rona, et al. "The Effects of Intermittent Energy Restriction on Indices of Cardiometabolic Health." *IBIMA Publishing,* June 28, 2014. http://ibimapublishing.com/articles/ENDO/2014/459119/

[68] Ho, K.Y., et al. "Fasting Enhances Growth Hormone Secretion and Amplifies the Complex Rhythms of Growth Hormone Secretion in Man." *US National Library of Medicine National Institutes of Health,* April 1988. https://www.ncbi.nlm.nih.gov/pmc/articles/PMC329619/

[69] Hartman, M.L., et al. "Augmented Growth Hormone (GH) Secretory Burst Frequency and Amplitude Mediate Enhanced GH Secretion During a Two-Day Fast in Normal Men." *US National Library of Medicine National Institutes of Health,* April 1992. https://www.ncbi.nlm.nih.gov/pubmed/1548337

[70] Varady, Krista A. and Marc K. Hellerstein. "Alternate-Day Fasting and Chronic Disease Prevention: a Review of Human and Animal Trials." *The American Journal of Clinical Nutrition,* July 2007. http://ajcn.nutrition.org/content/86/1/7.full

[71] Halagappa, V.K., et al. "Intermittent Fasting and Caloric Restriction Ameliorate Age-Related Behavioral Deficits in the Triple-Transgenic Mouse Model of Alzheimer's Disease." *US National Library of Medicine National Institutes of Health,* January 13, 2007. https://www.ncbi.nlm.nih.gov/pubmed/17306982

[72] Stipp, David. "How Intermittent Fasting Might Help You Live a Longer and Healthier Life." *Scientific American,* January 1, 2013. https://www.scientificamerican.com/article/how-intermittent-fasting-might-help-you-live-longer-healthier-life/

[73] Hinckley, David. "Average American Watches 5 Hours of TV per Day, Report Shows." *Daily News,* March 5, 2014. http://www.nydailynews.com/life-style/average-american-watches-5-hours-tv-day-article-1.1711954

Chapter 7

[74] "Meditation Makes You More Creative, Study Suggests." *Science Daily*, October 28, 2014. https://www.sciencedaily.com/releases/2014/10/141028082355.htm

[75] Rothschild, Bianca. "How Mindful Meditation Boosts Creativity and Innovation." *Huffington Post*, September 24, 2014. https://www.huffingtonpost.com/bianca-rothschild/the-science-of-how-medita_b_5579901.html

[76] "6 Ways Meditation Increases Your Intelligence & Raises Your IQ." *EOC Institute*. https://eocinstitute.org/meditation/increase-your-intelligence-with-meditation/

[77] Rankin, Lissa. "9 Key Factors Affecting Radical Remission From Cancer." *Lissa Rankin*, March 18, 2014. http://lissarankin.com/9-key-factors-affecting-radical-remission-from-cancer

[78] Turner, Kelly A., PhD. *Radical Remission: Surviving Cancer Against All Odds*. Harper One. 2015.

[79] Kam-Hansen, Slavenka, et al. "Altered Placebo and Drug Labeling Changes the Outcome of Episodic Migraine Attacks." *Science Translational Medicine*. *American Association for the Advancement of Science, January 8, 2014. http://stm.sciencemag.org/content/6/218/218ra5*

[80] Rankin, Lissa. "The Nocebo Effect: How Negative Thoughts Can Harm Your Health." *Lissa Rankin*, January 14, 2013. http://lissarankin.com/the-nocebo-effect-how-negative-thoughts-can-harm-your-health

[81] Deano. "Rogaine Study Sent to Me by Johnson & Johnson." January 25, 2008. http://www.hairlosshelp.com/forums/textthread.cfm?catid=10&threadid=75813

[82] Rankin, Lissa. "The Nocebo Effect: How Negative Thoughts Can Harm Your Health." *Lissa Rankin*, January 14, 2013. http://lissarankin.com/the-nocebo-effect-how-negative-thoughts-can-harm-your-health

[83] Rankin, Lissa. "The Nocebo Effect: How Negative Thoughts Can Harm Your Health." *Lissa Rankin*, January 14, 2013. http://lissarankin.com/the-nocebo-effect-how-negative-thoughts-can-harm-your-health

[84] "Spontaneous Remission Bibliography Project." *Institute of Noetic Sciences*, 1996. http://noetic.org/research/projects/spontaneous-remission

Chapter 8

[85] Kox, Matthijs, et al. "Voluntary Activation of the Sympathetic Nervous System and Attenuation of the Innate Immune Response in Humans." *National Academy of Sciences*, March 14, 2014. http://www.pnas.org/content/111/20/7379.long

[86] "The Heart: Views from the Past." *Institute of Traditional Medicine.* http://www.itmonline.org/5organs/heart.htm

[87] "The Heart: Views from the Past." *Institute of Traditional Medicine.* http://www.itmonline.org/5organs/heart.htm

[88] "The Heart: Views from the Past." *Institute of Traditional Medicine.* http://www.itmonline.org/5organs/heart.htm

[89] "Science of the Heart." *HeartMath Institute.* https://www.heartmath.org/research/science-of-the-heart/heart-brain-communication/

[90] You Can Change Your DNA." *HeartMath Institute*, July 14, 2011. https://www.heartmath.org/articles-of-the-heart/personal-development/you-can-change-your-dna/

[91] "Can We Permanently Stop Terrorism and War?" *Permanent Peace.* http://permanentpeace.org/

[92] "Meditation, the Key to World Peace." *World Peace Group.* http://www.worldpeacegroup.org/

[93] "Can We Permanently Stop Terrorism and War?" *Permanent Peace.* http://permanentpeace.org/

[94] Nicol, David. *Subtle Activism.* State University of NY Press. 2015. (Pg 107)

[95] "World Peace Research" http://www.worldpeacegroup.org/world_peace_research.html

Chapter 9

[96] Zheng, Xue, et al. "The Unburdening Effects of Forgiveness." *Sage Journals. Social and Personality Psychology Consortium*, December 23, 2014. http://journals.sagepub.com/doi/abs/10.1177/1948550614564222

Printed in Great Britain
by Amazon

74610566R00169